Table of Contents

Introduction to Fire Origin and Cause
Third Edition

Lynne Murnane
Project Manager/Editor

Thomas P. Ruane
Senior Editor

RECYCLABLE

Validated by the International Fire Service
Training Association

Published by Fire Protection Publications
Oklahoma State University

Cover photo courtesy of Donny Howard, Yates & Associates.

The International Fire Service Training Association

The International Fire Service Training Association (IFSTA) was established in 1934 as a "nonprofit educational association of fire fighting personnel who are dedicated to upgrading fire fighting techniques and safety through training." To carry out the mission of IFSTA, Fire Protection Publications was established as an entity of Oklahoma State University. Fire Protection Publications' primary function is to publish and disseminate training texts as proposed and validated by IFSTA. As a secondary function, Fire Protection Publications researches, acquires, produces, and markets high-quality learning and teaching aids as consistent with IFSTA's mission.

The IFSTA Validation Conference is held the second full week in July. Committees of technical experts meet and work at the conference addressing the current standards of the National Fire Protection Association and other standard-making groups as applicable. The Validation Conference brings together individuals from several related and allied fields, such as:

- Key fire department executives and training officers
- Educators from colleges and universities
- Representatives from governmental agencies
- Delegates of firefighter associations and industrial organizations

Committee members are not paid nor are they reimbursed for their expenses by IFSTA or Fire Protection Publications. They participate because of commitment to the fire service and its future through training. Being on a committee is prestigious in the fire service community, and committee members are acknowledged leaders in their fields. This unique feature provides a close relationship between the International Fire Service Training Association and fire protection agencies which helps to correlate the efforts of all concerned.

IFSTA manuals are now the official teaching texts of most of the states and provinces of North America. Additionally, numerous U.S. and Canadian government agencies as well as other English-speaking countries have officially accepted the IFSTA manuals.

ISBN 0-87939-252-5   *Library of Congress Control Number: 2005921666*

Third Edition, First Printing, April 2005   *Printed in the United States of America*

10   9   8   7   6   5   4   3   2   1

If you need additional information concerning the International Fire Service Training Association (IFSTA) or Fire Protection Publications, contact:

Customer Service, Fire Protection Publications, Oklahoma State University
930 North Willis, Stillwater, OK 74078-8045
800-654-4055   Fax: 405-744-8204

For assistance with training materials, to recommend material for inclusion in an IFSTA manual, or to ask questions or comment on manual content, contact:

Editorial Department, Fire Protection Publications, Oklahoma State University
930 North Willis, Stillwater, OK 74078-8045
405-744-4111   Fax: 405-744-4112   E-mail: editors@osufpp.org

Preface

Determining the origin and cause of a fire is not necessarily a simple process. Sometimes the cause of the fire is obvious to fire officers who are first in on the scene. At other times, determining the origin and cause will necessitate the help of experienced fire investigators who are law enforcement or fire department personnel. This manual is designed to assist emergency response personnel in identifying and preserving fire scene evidence and in determining when to call for the assistance of more highly trained fire investigators.

Acknowledgment and special thanks are extended to the members of the material review committee who contributed their time, wisdom, and knowledge to the development of this new third edition of **Introduction to Fire Origin and Cause.**

IFSTA Introduction to Fire Origin and Cause 3rd Edition Validation Committee

Chair

David Smith
President
Associated Fire Consultants Inc.
Tucson, AZ

Vice Chair/Secretary

Terry Dawn Hewitt
Barrister & Solicitor and
Attorney-at-Law
McKenna Hewitt
Denver, CO

Thomas Aurnhammer
Deputy Chief
Los Pinos Fire District
Ignacio, CO

John Blaschik
Deputy State Fire Marshal
Office of the State Fire Marshal
Middletown, CT

Joseph Carey
Attorney
Robinson & Cole LLP
Stamford, CT

Russell Chandler
VFMA Chief
Virginia Fire Marshal Academy
Virginia Department of Fire Programs
Glenn Allen, VA

Michael Donahue
Adjunct Professor-Fire Science
Montgomery College
Rockville, MD

Donny Howard
Associate/Investigator
Yates & Associates
Owasso, OK

Patrick Kennedy
Chairman
National Association of Fire Investigators
Sarasota, FL

Loren Lippincott
Fire and EMS Coordinator
Blackhawk Technical College
Janesville, WI

Kim May
Engineering Manager
Barker & Herbert Analytical Laboratories, Inc.
New Haven, IN

Michael Schulz
President
M.J. Schulz & Associates, Inc.
Bartlett, IL

Bruce Peacock
Training Officer
Toronto Fire Services
Toronto, Ontario, Canada

Dennis Smith
Investigator
Kodiak Enterprises, Inc.
Fort Wayne, IN

Robert Rose
Chief Fire Marshal
Department of Public Safety Services
Burlington County New Jersey
Mt. Holly, NJ

G. Terry Smith
Fire Investigator
EFI - Engineering and Fire Investigations
Ely, IA

Grateful thanks is also extended to the following organizations and individuals who contributed information, photographs, and technical assistance that were instrumental in the development of this manual:

Donny Howard, Yates and Associates, for supplying numerous photographs

Chris E. Mickal, New Orleans Fire Department Photo Unit, LA

Connecticut Office of State Fire Marshal, Middletown, CT

Bonnie Hudlet, photographer

Barker & Herbert Analytical Laboratories, Inc.

Last, but certainly not least, gratitude is extended to the following members of the Fire Protection Publications staff whose contributions made the final publication of this manual possible:

Jeff Fortney, Senior Editor

Cindy Brakhage, Senior Editor

Tara Gladden, Editorial Assistant

Robin Balderson, Staff Assistant

Foster Cryer, Research Technician

Don Davis, Production Manager

Ann Moffat, Senior Graphic Analyst

Clint Parker, Senior Graphic Designer

Introduction

The incidence of fire continues to plague our society, exacting a devastating toll on our neighbors as well as on the emergency response personnel who respond to protect them. Families are left homeless, jobs are lost, and monetary losses can be devastating. The impact on society from loss due to fire continues to be significant. Emergency response personnel have the responsibility to employ a systematic approach toward fire scene analysis, evidence collection and preservation, report generation, and data analysis. The information generated by the work of these initial responders is crucial to the conduct of an accurate fire investigation. The information generated by the initial scene examination can be used to determine the origin of the fire and how it started. Additionally, an investigation can fix responsibility for the fire, either as an accidental event or one that was intentionally set. From the initial investigation, the information gathered can form the basis for sound courtroom testimony in both civil and criminal trials brought before the court. The outcomes of these legal proceedings help reduce the potential for additional fire resulting from arson, by removing the responsible individual from society, or by eliminating a defective device or process from general public use.

Incomplete scene examination or inaccurate reports, on the other hand, undermine the credibility of statistical data when conducting a fire trend analysis. Risk identification and preventative measures, based on this data, cannot be developed that accurately reflect potential fire risk factors. This will result in a flawed analysis, followed by bad assumptions and incorrect solutions. The credibility of the investigation system rests with the proper employment of an investigative methodology that seeks to systematically and objectively find the truth by adhering to standard procedures that create a record of the events that lead up to the fire and the subsequent investigation. Unintentional inaccuracies usually result from inattention or a lack of understanding regarding the necessity of accuracy by the report writer.

Beyond the normal combustion process described in Chapter 3, Fire Behavior, the cause of fire is a combination of three factors:

- The type of fuel ignited
- The form and source of the heat of ignition
- An act or omission that allowed a fire to start

Knowing the cause of a fire helps the fire department to prevent similar occurrences in the future. Careful investigative procedures including reports on innocuous-appearing fire events will allow the department to analyze fire experience inside of their jurisdiction. Resources can then be allocated to reduce the number of fire incidents. Subsequently, a decrease of the number of incidents experienced and reduction in loss of life and property will diminish the human and economic impact of fire on the community.

Firefighters on the scene have the best opportunity to observe the nature and behavior of the fire during suppression operations. This provides unique opportunity to identify and preserve items that can lead to an accurate determination of the location where the fire started as well as its cause. The firefighter/first responder provides an invaluable link to fire/arson investigators and law enforcement agencies by laying a strong investigative foundation early in the incident. A professionally conducted fire investigation should seek to identify the following:

- The location where the heat source and fuel came together – the point of origin
- The recognition of the conditions or circumstances that brought together the fuel, heat source, and air – the cause
- Flame, heat and smoke spread characteristics within the structure
- Who or what was responsible for the fire
- Were unusual hazards or dangerous conditions presented to the firefighters
- What corrective actions can be recommended as a result of the investigation

Purpose and Scope

The purpose of this manual is to provide a guide for emergency response personnel (ERPs) who are charged with trying to determine the origin and cause of a fire. This manual is intended to provide company officers, firefighters and other emergency response personnel with information that will assist them in this process. This manual provides guidelines for ERPs who are on the scene during and immediately after a fire. They are likely to be called on to know any of all of the following:

- Recognize conditions during the fire investigation that may pose an imminent safety hazard.
- Use personal protective equipment and devices to prevent injury from risks associated with fire scenes.
- Understand the responsibilities of emergency response personnel with regard to mitigating the fire and examining and preserving the scene afterward.
- Understand basic fire chemistry and its behavior.
- Observe and record the conditions pertinent to the incident.
- Conduct a preliminary fire scene survey.
- Locate the area of origin, identify witnesses, and preserve possible evidence.
- Identify the material first ignited and the source of the heat of ignition.
- Make a probable determination of the cause of the fire and whether it was accidental or intentionally started.

- Ensure that the initial investigation follows acceptable legal practices.
- Initiate the investigative report and take appropriate follow-up actions.

This manual addresses the relevant portions of NFPA 1001, *Standard for Fire Fighter Professional Qualifications* and NFPA 1021, *Standard for Fire Officer Professional Qualifications*. It is also relevant to certain portions of the Emergency Responder Guidelines for the Office for Domestic Preparedness, Awareness Level. The knowledge and skills pertaining to each of these standards are printed in front of the chapters in which they are addressed. It also addresses certain portions of the Office for Domestic Preparedness (OPD) *Emergency Responder Guidelines*, 2002 Edition, for firefighters, law enforcement, and emergency medical personnel. These standards and guidelines are listed in front of the chapters in which they are addressed.

Key Information

Various types of information are given in shaded boxes marked by symbols or icons:

Sidebars give additional relevant information that is more detailed, descriptive, or explanatory than that given in the text.

Information boxes give facts that are complete in themselves but belong with the text discussion. They include information that may need additional emphasis or separation.

Safety reminders call attention to safety information that deserves extra emphasis or repetition.

Chapter 1:
Safety

Courtesy of Donny Howard, Yates & Associates.

Job Performance Requirements

This chapter provides information that will assist the reader in meeting the following performance requirements from NFPA 1001, *Fire Fighter Professional Qualifications*, 2002 edition and NFPA 1021, *Standard for Fire Officer Professional Qualifications*, 2003 edition. Boldfaced portions of the standard are specifically addressed in this chapter.

NFPA 1001

Chapter 5, Fire Fighter I

5.3 Fireground Operations

This duty involves performing activities necessary to ensure life safety, fire control, and property conservation, according to the following job performance requirements.

5.3.1* Use SCBA during emergency operations, given SCBA and other personal protective equipment, so that the SCBA is correctly donned and activated within one minute, the SCBA is correctly worn, controlled breathing techniques are used, emergency procedures are enacted if the SCBA fails, all low-air warnings are recognized, respiratory protection is not intentionally compromised, and hazardous areas are exited prior to air depletion.

   (A) **Requisite Knowledge. Conditions that require respiratory protection, uses and limitations of SCBA,** components of SCBA, donning procedures, breathing techniques, indications for and emergency procedures used with SCBA, and physical requirements of the SCBA wearer.

5.3.2* Respond on apparatus to an emergency scene, given personal protective clothing and other necessary personal protective equipment, so that the apparatus is correctly mounted and dismounted, seat belts are used while the vehicle is in motion, and other **personal protective equipment is correctly used**.

   (A) **Requisite Knowledge.** Mounting and dismounting procedures for riding fire apparatus; hazards and ways to avoid hazards associated with riding apparatus; prohibited practices; **types of department personal protective equipment and the means for usage**.

   (B) **Requisite Skills. The ability to use each piece of provided safety equipment.**

5.3.3* **Operate in established work areas at emergency scenes, given protective equipment, traffic and scene control devices, structure fire and roadway emergency scenes, traffic hazards and downed electrical wires, so that procedures are followed, protective equipment is worn, protected work areas are established as directed using traffic and scene control devices, and the fire fighter performs assigned tasks only in established, protected work areas.**

   (A) **Requisite Knowledge. Potential hazards involved in operating on emergency scenes including vehicle traffic, utilities, and environmental conditions; proper procedures for dismounting apparatus in traffic; procedures for safe operation at emergency scenes; and the**

protective equipment available for members' safety on emergency scenes and work zone designations.

   (B) **Requisite Skills.** The ability to use PPC, the deployment of traffic and scene control devices, dismount apparatus and operate in the protected work areas as directed.

5.3.8* Extinguish fires in exterior Class A materials, given fires in stacked or piled and small unattached structures or storage containers that can be fought from the exterior, attack lines, hand tools and master stream devices, and an assignment, so that exposures are protected, the spread of fire is stopped, collapse hazards are avoided, water application is effective, the fire is extinguished, and **signs of the origin area(s) and arson are preserved.**

   (A) **Requisite Knowledge.** Types of attack lines and water streams appropriate for attacking stacked, piled materials and outdoor fires; dangers — such as collapse — associated with stacked and piled materials; various extinguishing agents and their effect on different material configurations; tools and methods to use in breaking up various types of materials; the difficulties related to complete extinguishment of stacked and piled materials; water application methods for exposure protection and fire extinguishment; dangers such as exposure to toxic or hazardous materials associated with storage building and container fires; **obvious signs of origin and cause; and techniques for the preservation of fire cause evidence.**

   (B) **Requisite Skills.** The ability to recognize inherent hazards related to the material's configuration, operate handlines or master streams, break up material using hand tools and water streams, evaluate for complete extinguishment, operate hose lines and other water application devices, evaluate and modify water application for maximum penetration, search for and expose hidden fires, **assess patterns for origin determination, and evaluate for complete extinguishment.**

NFPA 1021

Chapter 4 Fire Officer I

4.7* Health and Safety.

This duty involves integrating safety plans, policies, and procedures into the daily activities as well as the emergency scene, including the donning of appropriate levels of personal protective equipment to ensure a work environment, in accordance with health and safety plans, for all assigned members, according to the following job performance requirements.

   (A) **Requisite Knowledge.** The most common causes of personal injury and accident to members, safety policies and procedures, basic workplace safety, and the components of an infectious disease control program.

Chapter 1
Safety

Emergency response personnel conducting a fire investigation are faced with the same hazards and dangers that firefighters encounter during suppression and overhaul operations. Constant vigilance by emergency response personnel for such hazards as structural stability, hazardous atmospheres, toxic materials, and the presence of combustion by-products, are as necessary during the fire investigation as it is during the suppression stage of the emergency. Beyond all other responsibilities, emergency response personnel must ensure that **ALL** precautions are taken to keep themselves and others at the incident scene safe from exposure to undue hazards. Injuries and illnesses resulting from exposure to these hazardous elements can be greatly reduced by making use of protective clothing, respiratory protection, and monitoring devices. Additionally, the investigation must be conducted within the framework of the operational procedures of the fire department. This includes the Incident Management System (IMS) and the personal accountability system as adopted by the local responding emergency agency.

> Throughout this manual the phrase *emergency response personnel* or ERP refers to the individuals initially responsible for the determination of the origin and cause of a fire or explosion, or to those individuals who respond to an emergency and must observe and protect evidence for any investigators who will follow.

All agencies and their personnel at the emergency scene must conform to regulations established by the Occupational Safety and Health Administration and/or the Environmental Protection Agency as well as those in the local jurisdiction. The umbrella of authority allowing access to the scenes extends from the local jurisdiction and agency through the emergency response personnel's employers to the employees themselves. In essence there are responsibilities and anticipated performances at each level in an organization to ensure safety. Safety policies and procedures must be continually enforced. In addition, organizations are responsible for delivering effective safety and health programs that address potential hazards that personnel may encounter while working at an emergency scene. After sound operating guidelines have been developed that conform to acceptable standards of practice, employees will be able to perform all investigative activities as safely as possible.

NOTE: For additional information about safety practices for investigators at emergency scenes, consult the FPP *Safety and Health Guidelines for Fire and Explosion Investigators* manual.

Safety Equipment

Regardless of the severity of an incident, ERPs must wear appropriate clothing and equipment to ensure their safety and well-being. As with all emergency responses, safety will be compromised if personal protective safety equipment is not available or if the equipment is not worn and used properly. The level of protection required is determined by the scene and the hazards that can be anticipated during the investigation. A minimum level of protection must always be met: protection for the head, eyes, hands, and feet is essential.

Depending upon conditions at the scene, increased protection may be necessary. This protection could include full structural fire fighting protective equipment or chemical protective clothing with positive pressure self-contained breathing apparatus (SCBA).

In some instances where there is a risk of nuclear, biological, or chemical exposure, a higher and more specialized level of personal protection may be required. *It must be remembered that all protective equipment has inherent limitations.* ERPs must select the appropriate protective clothing designed to provide protection against the hazards present. **Training in the use of these protective ensembles is essential to ensure that this equipment is used and maintained to provide optimal performance.**

Personal Protective Equipment

Although a fire may be under control, many hazards remain. Personnel involved with an investigation often fail to realize that they face conditions very similar to those encountered by fire suppression crews. The use of structural fire fighting gear, namely personal protective equipment (PPE), provides a level of protection that offers an additional barrier to abrasions, cuts, minor burns, and possible impact from falling objects. Because the possibility of hidden "hot spots" and other hazards is a real one immediately following suppression and overhaul activities, the ERP should avoid the use of nonapproved coveralls and lightweight shoes or boots. If the preliminary investigation is extended and it is determined that burn and impact risks have been minimized or removed, the ERP should wear flame-resistant (FR) coveralls or trousers and shirts. Steel-toed boots, helmets, and gloves should always be worn while conducting an investigation **(Figure 1.1)**.

There should be constant vigilance in monitoring the atmosphere and the structural conditions. The continued use of atmospheric and chemical monitoring devices should be maintained throughout the incident. Severe circumstances involving possible toxic atmospheres or hazardous materials may necessitate the donning of an appropriate chemical protective suit and complete respiratory protection before entering the "hot zone" to even begin an investigation. It is essential that emergency response personnel be trained both to recognize the level of hazard present and to use safety equipment prop-

Figure 1.1 Emergency response personnel must remember to wear proper protective clothing during all phases of the fire investigation.

erly. Although no protective ensemble can totally eliminate all risks present at the incident scene, the use of quality, National Fire Protection Association (NFPA) compliant PPE may reduce the possibility of injury to the ERP.

National Fire Protection Association (NFPA)

The NFPA is an organization concerned with fire safety standards development, technical advisory services, education, research, and other related services. Its members come from the educational and scientific sectors of the fire protection field, both private and public. The NFPA's primary service to the fire protection field is the development of technical consensus standards. The NFPA, which was organized in 1896, also develops fire training and public fire education materials.

Address: 1 Batterymarch Park, P.O. Box 9101, Quincy, MA 02169-7471

Web site: www.nfpa.org

Bunker Coats and Trousers

Structural fire fighting turnouts (bunker gear) are generally suitable for post-fire activities. Wearing bunker gear protects the body from abrasions and cuts, minor burns, etc. All bunker coats and trousers should meet the standards set forth in NFPA 1971, *Standard on Protective Ensemble for Structural Fire Fighting.*

 Remember that bunker gear may absorb liquids and become saturated. Some hazardous substances that are present at fire scenes, such as benzene, can permeate material and become absorbed into the skin.

Coveralls

Coveralls are versatile and can be worn over other clothing while providing a limited measure of protection, uniformity, and comfort. Coveralls do NOT provide the level of protection afforded by the structural fire fighting ensemble and they must be thought of as simply an additional layer of clothing. If the fire is still burning, or there is a further risk of fire, the coveralls should be made of a flame-resistant fabric or treated with a flame-resistant substance, and additionally should comply with NFPA 1975, *Standard on Station/Work Uniforms for Fire and Emergency Services.*

 Clothing used on the fireground should be considered contaminated and cleaned in the appropriate manner. See the IFSTA **Essentials** manual for a discussion of cleaning contaminated clothing.

Helmets and Hard Hats

Damage caused by either the fire itself or by fire fighting activities may weaken structural supports and other building materials. Therefore, head protection must be one of the first concerns of emergency response personnel. An emergency responder should always wear either a hard hat or a fire helmet for protection from falling debris. Hard hats should meet the requirements of ANSI Standard Z89.1 and OSHA (OH&S Canada) regula-

tions. If fire helmets are worn, they should meet the specifications set forth in NFPA 1971, *Standard on Protective Ensemble for Structural Fire Fighting.*

Gloves

The most important characteristics of gloves are the protection they provide against heat or cold penetration and their resistance to cuts, punctures, and liquid permeation. This can be accomplished by wearing latex gloves under strong durable leather gloves. During investigations it is almost always necessary to sift through such debris as broken glass, charred furniture, and so on. In addition, some of the material may still be too hot to handle without protection. Gloves must fit properly and provide protection as well as affording dexterity, including enough tactile feel to perform the job effectively (**Figures 1.2 a - c**). If the gloves are too awkward and bulky, the ERP may be unable to do fine, manipulative work. NFPA

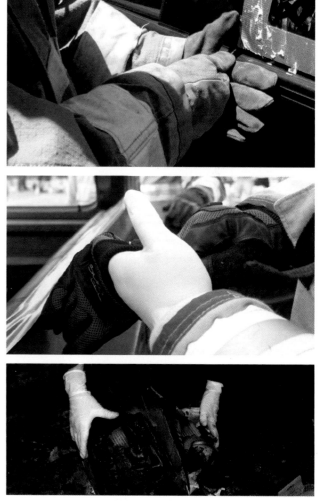

Figures 1.2 a-c Different types of gloves may allow ERPs to carefully handle potential evidence. *C courtesy of Donny Howard, Yates & Associates.*

1971, *Standard on Protective Ensemble for Structural Fire Fighting,* provides the requirements for gloves for ERPs.

Boots

During post-fire activities, ERPs may encounter such hazards as falling objects and smoldering fire brands. The ERP should select appropriate foot protection to ensure that the risk of injury from these hazards is minimized. Normal turnout boots may be sufficient for post-fire activities. Boots should provide adequate toe and midsole protection, so boots that have a full steel plate to deflect nails are best. Turnout boots should meet the requirements of NFPA 1971, *Standard on Protective Ensemble for Structural Fire Fighting.*

Hazardous Atmospheres

All emergency response personnel will be confronted with hazardous atmospheres and the concentration of toxic fire gases often increases after the fire has been extinguished. Partially consumed materials continue to produce these by-products even after the flames have been extinguished. If the emergency involved explosives, their detonation or deflagration, as well as the rapid exothermic reaction of other chemicals, will generate large volumes of toxic gases. The ERP must be prepared to recognize and operate safely in these potentially lethal atmospheres.

Respiratory Protection

Emergency response personnel must ensure that they are not exposed to toxic atmospheres. The traditional risks presented by fire and chemical manufacturing processes have expanded to include additional threats posed by potential terrorist acts. Unfortunately, predicting the kind and type of hazardous agent to be faced, whether chemical or biological, is difficult if not impossible until the onset of the incident. As has been painfully learned during recent terrorist events, many of the available respiratory protective devices work very well for some situations, but not as well for others. ERPs may need to have available several respirators for different hazards (**Figures 1.3 a - c**). Even with constant atmospheric monitoring of the emergency scene, the ERP must remain cautious and use prudence while working in these

Figures 1.3 a-c After a fire, atmospheric conditions remain extremely hazardous. ERPs must be familiar with and wear appropriate respiratory protection. *a and c FEMA News Photo.*

environments, which pose the same health and life threats as loss control and overhaul operations do during fire suppression efforts. Smoldering fire and other degrading chemicals that are common at fire scenes can quickly debilitate and incapacitate inadequately protected individuals, leading to major injury or death. Hazardous materials, clandestine drug labs, and entomologic incidents constitute special respiratory requirements. ERPs must have available and be prepared to use respiratory protection equipment as a precaution against the harmful effects of atmospheric exposure to potential life and health safety risks.

Even fire scenes with no burning or smoldering fires present a considerable risk to ERPs. When the debris from a fire scene is disturbed, some particles, such as asbestos, become airborne and susceptible to inhalation. Common particulates such as carbon (soot) are considered to be a cancer risk in large quantities. Atmospheres with sufficient oxygen and low or undetectable gas hazards still require respiratory protection. The individual must use a filter mask with maximum protection filters. These dust particulates can also be absorbed through the sclera of the eye. For this reason it is important to use a full filter mask or a half mask with non-vented goggles.

NOTE: For more information on respiratory protection, consult the IFSTA **Respiratory Protection for Fire and Emergency Services** manual.

> # WARNING!
> Emergency response personnel must be aware that potentially lethal atmospheres exist even as a fire is brought under control. All personnel entering a structure must wear appropriate respiratory protection.

Atmospheric Monitoring Devices
The particular toxic gases that may be found at fire and explosion sites vary according to four common factors:

- Nature of the combustible
- Rate of heating
- Temperature of the evolved gases
- Oxygen concentration

Monitors for testing atmospheric conditions are available and should be used before anyone is allowed to enter an area where the atmosphere may be immediately dangerous to life and health (IDLH). Several types of monitoring devices can be used to test the atmosphere for hazardous gases. These devices include the following: (**Figures 1.4 a - c, p.10**).

- Multi-gas personal monitor
- Detector tubes
- Combustible gas indicators
- Multi-specific gas detectors (including O_2, CO, etc.)
- Radiation detectors

Atmospheric monitors provide ERPs with the information they need to effectively protect themselves from the hazards present at the scene. These versatile devices are designed to detect and/or measure multiple gases and hazardous atmospheres that may be encountered. They provide information such as the type and relative quantity of hazard present. From this information, the ERP can determine the type of personal protective clothing and equipment required to safely carry out the investigation until the hazards are eliminated.

Ionizing Radiation
Radioactive materials may be present at fire scenes involving medical facilities or laboratories and emit one or more of the three types of harmful radiation (**Figure 1.5, p.10**):

- Alpha particles
- Beta particles
- Gamma rays

Alpha particle radiation usually does not penetrate beyond clothing or the outer layer of the skin. If it is prevented from entering the body it will cause little damage. Beta radiation causes burning on the skin surface and damage to the subsurface skin circulatory system. Both alpha and beta particles can be extremely dangerous if they find their way into the body. Gamma radiation, however, passes through clothing and tissue causing severe, permanent injury to the body.

Figures 1.4 a – c Atmospheric monitoring devices are a must for hazardous atmospheres.

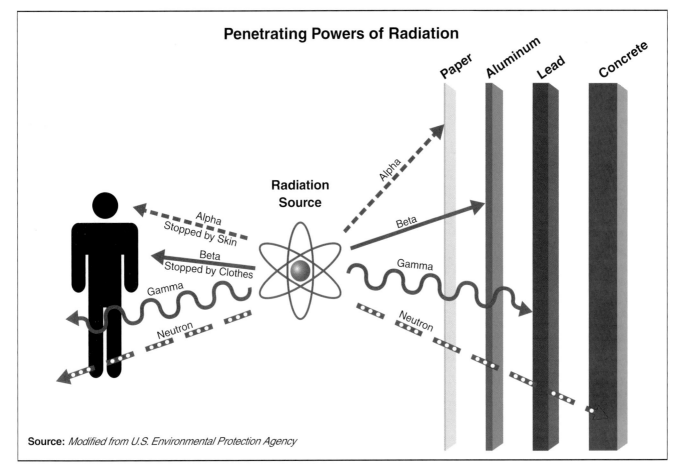

Figure 1.5 Gamma rays are the most penetrating and harmful types of radiation.

///////////////////////

WARNING!

Structural fire fighting bunker gear and chemical protective suits afford <u>no</u> protective barrier against gamma radiation. Use of respirators will reduce and may prevent radioactive materials from entering the body.

Figure 1.6 Emergency responders must receive regular rest and fluids if they are to remain effective on the emergency scene.

Health and Rehab

The environment will dictate the precautions necessary to maintain a healthy balance at the fire scene. In frigid conditions steps should be taken to have an occasional warmer environment to rest and replenish liquids as well as an occasional snack to provide energy. Of course this place of rest must be remote enough to ensure a safe atmosphere as well as provide facilities for ERPs to wash up to prevent contamination during the ingestion of any liquids or foods.

Likewise in warmer weather the ERP must take into account not only the ambient temperature but also the increased heat from wearing protective clothing. Frequent breaks outside the fire scene will be necessary to ensure adequate hydration, rest, and occasional snacks to provide energy **(Figure 1.6)**. Cleanliness is essential to ensure there is no contamination of drinks or foods either in handling or during ingestion.

Hazardous Materials

Emergency operations may be conducted at the scene of a hazardous materials (haz mat) incident. A *hazardous material*, as defined by the U.S. Department of Transportation in 49 *CFR* 171.8, is "a substance or material, including a hazardous substance, that has been determined by the Secretary of Transportation to be capable of posing an unreasonable risk to health, safety, and property when transported in commerce, and which has been so designated."

Because hazardous materials may be encountered at any time, the ERP must not be lulled into entering a life-threatening situation. The commanding officer must initially survey the scene and make the decision that the scene does not pose a threat. It may be a wise decision just to walk away from the scene if it cannot be entered safely.

The ERP should have a basic understanding of the ways in which to identify potential hazards. The ERP must also determine whether the area is safe or whether specialized assistance is necessary before entering the area. The priority is self-protection. Emergency responders should carry binoculars in the vehicle that they can use to evaluate the safety of the situation while maintaining a safe distance from the scene. For incidents involving vehicles that are transporting hazardous materials, the ERP can look for placards to help identify the material(s) in question. *Placards* are diamond-shaped signs that are affixed to each side of a vehicle transporting hazardous materials **(Figure 1.7, p. 12)**. The placard indicates the primary class of the material and, in some cases, the exact material transported.

Hazardous materials that are manufactured, stored, processed, or used at a particular site are not subject to the same regulations affecting transported materials. Local agencies and county, city, and township governments may adopt their own identification system. Alternatively, they may decide to use a widely recognized method such as that recommended by NFPA 704, *Standard System*

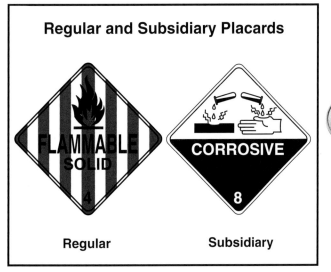

Regular and Subsidiary Placards

Regular   Subsidiary

Figure 1.7 Placards on vehicles provide a quick source of information about the dangers of the cargo being transported.

for the Identification of the Hazards of Materials for Emergency Response (**Figure 1.8**). The ratings for each hazard (health, flammability, and instability) are described in the standard itself. Some private companies and the military have their own policies that regulate the marking of these materials.

NOTE: For more information on the NFPA 704 marking system, consult the **IFSTA Hazardous Materials for First Responders** or the **Awareness Level Training for Hazardous Materials** manuals.

All flammable and combustible materials maintained in a facility must be inventoried and have material safety data sheets (MSDS) collected on each item (**Figure 1.9**). This information must be kept in an MSDS book on the site, and it must contain health, safety, and injury prevention information. Personnel must be trained in the use of the flammable and combustible liquids and the MSDS book.

Whether the incident involves a vehicle or a fixed facility, the ERP's actions should be the same. If the incident involves a release or spill of a hazardous chemical, the ERP should observe the scene from a safe distance and wait for the area to be declared safe to enter. For more information on hazardous materials identification, refer to the IFSTA **Hazardous Materials for First Responders** manual.

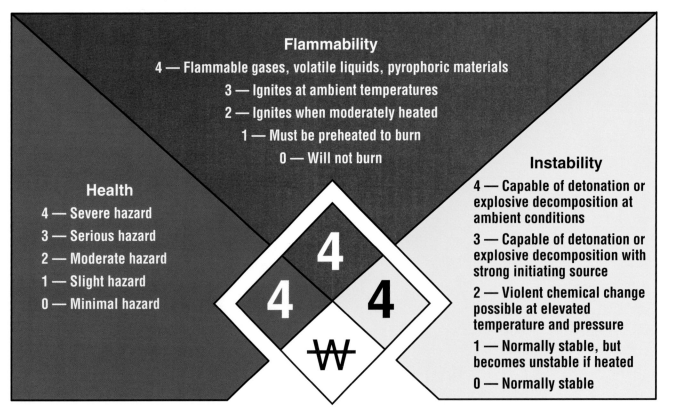

Figure 1.8 The NFPA 704 system is commonly used for hazardous materials stored in fixed facilities.

Material Safety Data Sheet

Hoechst Celanese

Chemical Group
Hoechst Celanese Corporation
*P.O. Box 819005/Dallas, Texas 75381-9005
*Information phone: 214 277 4000
Emergency phone: 800 424 9300 (CHEMTREC)

Ethylene oxide

Issued December 31, 1992 #40

Identification

Product name: Ethylene oxide
Chemical name: Ethylene oxide
Chemical family: Epoxide
Formula: $(CH_2)_2O$
Molecular weight: 44
CAS number: 75-21-8
CAS name: Oxirane
Synonyms: Dihydrooxirene; dimethylene oxide; 1,2-epoxyethane; oxiran; oxirane; oxacyclopropane; oxane; oxidoethane; alpha, beta-oxidoethane; EO; EtO.

*Transportation information
Shipping name: Ethylene Oxide
Hazard class: 2.3, Poisonous Gas
Subsidiary hazard: 2.1, Flammable Gas
United Nations no.: UN1040
Packing group: 1
Emergency Response Guide no.: 69
DOT Reportable Quantity: 10 lb/4.54 kg

Physical data

Boiling point (760 mm Hg): 10.7°C (51°F)
Freezing point: -112.5°C (-171°F)
Specific gravity (H_2O=1 @ 20/20°C): 0.8711
Vapor pressure (20°C): 1094 mm Hg
Vapor density (Air =1 @ 20°C): 1.5
Solubility in water (% by WT @ 20°C): Complete
Percent volatiles by volume: 100
Appearance and odor: Colorless gas with sweet ether-like odor. Odor threshold: 500 ppm.

Fire and explosion hazard data

Flammable limits in air, % by volume
Upper: 100
Lower: 3.0

Flash point (test method):
Tag open cup (ASTM D1310): <0°F (<−18°C)
Tag closed cup (ASTM D56): −4°F (−20°C)

Extinguishing media:
Use water (flood with water), CO_2, dry chemical or alcohol-type aqueous film-forming foam. Allow to burn if flow cannot be shut off immediately.

Special fire-fighting procedures:
*If potential for exposure to vapors

*New or revised information; previous version dated October 1, 1991.

Component information (See Glossary at end of MSDS for definitions)

Component, wt. % (CAS number)	Exposure levels			Subject to SARA §313 reporting?
	OSHA PEL TWA	ACGIH TLV ®TWA	IDLH	
• Ethylene oxide, 99.95% (75-21-8)	1ppm[2]; 5 ppm excursion limit	1ppm[2]	800 ppm	Yes

(1) All components listed as required by federal, California, New Jersey and Pennsylvania regulations.
(2) Suspectd human carcinogen.

or products of combustion exists, wear complete personal protective equipment, including self-contained breathing apparatus with full facepiece operated in pressure-demand or other positive-pressure mode.

Dilution of ethylene oxide with 23 volumes of water renders it non-flammable. A ratio of 100 parts water to one part ethylene oxide may be required to control build-up of flammable vapors in a closed system. Water spray can be used to reduce intensity of flames and to dilute spills to nonflammable mixture. Use water spray to cool fire-exposed structures and vessels. Ethylene oxide is an NFPA Class 1A flammable liquid with a 51°F boiling point. Locations classified as hazardous because of the presence of ethylene oxide are designated Class 1.

Unusual fire and explosion hazards:
Rapid, uncontrolled polymerization can cause explosion under fire conditions. Vapor is heavier than air and can travel considerable distance to a source of ignition and flashback. Will burn without the presence of air or other oxidizers.

Special hazard designations

	HMIS	NFPA	Key
Health:	3	3	0 = Minimal
Flammability:	4	4	1 = Slight
Reactivity:	3	3	2 = Moderate
Personal protective equipment:	G	—	3 = Serious
			4 = Severe

SARA §311 hazard categories
Acute health:	Yes
Chronic health:	Yes
Fire:	Yes
Sudden release of pressure:	Yes
Reactive:	Yes

Reactivity data

Stability:
Potentially unstable

Hazardous polymerization:
Can occur.UNCONTROLLED POLYMERIZATION CAN CAUSE RAPID EVOLUTION OF HEAT AND INCREASED PRESSURE WHICH CAN RESULT IN VIOLENT RUPTURE OF STORAGE VESSELS OR CONTAINERS.

Conditions to avoid:
Heat, sparks, flame.

Materials to avoid:
Acetylide-forming metals (for example, copper, silver, mercury and their alloys): alcohols; amines; mercaptans; metallic chlorides; aqueous alkalis; mineral acids; oxides; strong oxidizing agents (for example, oxygen, hydrogen peroxide, or nitric acid).

Hazardous combustion or decomposition products:
Carbon monoxide.

Health data

Effects of exposure/toxicity data
  Acute

Ingestion (swallowing): Can cause stomach irritation, also liver and kidney damage. Moderately toxic to animals (oral LD_{50}, rats: 0.1 g/kg).

Inhalation (breathing): Can cause irritation of nasal passages, throat and lungs; lung injury; nausea; vomiting; headache; diarrhea; shortness of breath; cyanosis (blue or purple coloring of the skin); and pulmonary edema (accumulation of fluid in the lungs) - signs and symptons can be delayed for several hours. Slightly toxic to animals (inhalation LC_{50}, rats, 4 hrs: 1460 ppm).

Skin contact: Can lead to severe reddening and swelling of the skin, with blisters.

Figure 1.9 Any information at the site concerning hazardous materials should be studied as part of the size-up process.

Biohazards

Emergency response personnel face potential exposure to biological hazards in addition to blood, body fluids, and other potentially infectious materials present at the scene of a fire or explosion. Acquired immune deficiency syndrome (AIDS), caused by the human immunodeficiency virus (HIV), is perhaps the most widely publicized disease affecting ERP; however, hepatitis B possibly poses a more significant threat. The hepatitis virus is particularly threatening because it has been found to live several days in dried blood spills. Emergency response personnel can be exposed wherever blood, body fluid, or other contaminated equipment are present. Infection control procedures and body substance isolation recognize that *all* body fluids must be treated as if known to be infectious. The best method for preventing infection by biological agents is to provide a barrier between the person and the infectious agent by wearing disposable gloves, masks, gowns, and eye protection **(Figure 1.10)**. Where exposure is likely, such as scenes involving fatalities, the Occupational Safety and Health Administration (29 *CFR* 1910.1030, Bloodborne Pathogens) mandates a comprehensive program.

Figure 1.10 Enclosed suits are necessary to provide a barrier against biological hazards.

Always use disposable protective gloves, coveralls, and shoe covers when exposed to potentially infectious materials. Eye and faceshields should be worn to protect against exposure from infectious material splashes or sprays. Do not eat, drink, or smoke where blood, body fluid, or other potentially infectious materials are found. When removing protective equipment, ensure that exposed skin does not come in contact with contaminated exterior equipment surfaces. All equipment must be decontaminated after use on site. Items that are not intended for reuse must be disposed of in an approved manner that eliminates the possibility of remote contamination.

Incident Management System

The on-scene investigation, while separate from the actual job of mitigation of the fire scene, remains a part of the incident, and therefore falls within the scope of incident management. The ERP does **NOT** operate outside of or independently from the established incident management organization at the scene. From the moment the ERPs arrive until the last unit is demobilized and returned to service, the incident scene is required to be within the control of the Incident Management System.

Incident Management System

In the United States, the Department of Homeland Security has adopted the National Incident Management System (NIMS) as a unifying organizational system for emergency responders and programs. For more information about NIMS, which is under the Federal Emergency Management Agency (FEMA), consult its web site: www.fema.gov/nims/index.shtm.

NOTE: The organizational structure and terms outlined in a number of FPP publications describing the Incident Management System are consistent with the guidelines stipulated by NIMS.

Scene Safety Precautions

The potential for injury to emergency responders on the scene of an emergency is extremely high. Moving vehicles, multiple task assignments, chaotic events, poor lighting, pressurized hoselines, disrupted utilities, uncontrolled animals, criminal

Figure 1.11 Dangers are always present at an emergency scene. ERPs must work together to minimize the risks of injury. *Courtesy of Chris E. Mickal.*

activity, as well as distraught individuals can cause injury or death to first responders and bystanders **(Figure 1.11)**. Preemptive caution must be exercised at all times, from the moment of notification until the incident has been demobilized. Some of the more common hazards that are likely to be encountered on scene are as follows **(Figures 1.12 a - e, p. 16)**:

- Damaged structural members / falling debris
- Ignition sources
- Broken glass, nails or torn metal
- Holes in floors
- Hanging light fixtures
- Exposed ("energized") electrical wiring (underground, overhead, and residential services)
- Damaged electrical appliances or equipment
- Damaged natural gas/propane lines
- High noise levels

- Environmental factors (particularly such weather conditions as extreme cold or heat, lightning storms, etc., loose flooring or steps, slippery surfaces, and protruding objects
- Unsecured objects that can fall from elevated surfaces
- Confined spaces

NOTE: For a more comprehensive discussion of on-scene hazards and precautions, consult the FPP *Safety and Health Guidelines for Fire and Explosion Investigators* manual.

Rekindle

There is always a threat of rekindle at a fire scene. The ERP must always be aware of two exits from any location within the fire ground. Special care must be taken to prevent entrapment when in or around concealed spaces or crawl spaces.

Figures 1.12 a – e Common hazards at fire emergency scenes include hanging debris; falling/tripping hazards; weakened floors, ceilings, and roofs; exposed insulation; electrical hazards; and fire debris that is dangerous to walk around or work in. *All photos courtesy of Donny Howard, Yates & Associates.*

Structural Stability

Structural stability is critical to the safety of all emergency response personnel. The ERP should reassess the scene before attempting any investigation to determine fire origin or cause. Conduct an examination of all exterior surfaces in order to determine that the building is sound before entering. Once inside, visually assess all walls, ceilings, chimneys, and floors **(Figure 1.13, p. 17)**. Watch for chimneys, whether visible or hidden. As the scene is examined and debris is moved, structural stability must be continually reassessed. For example, what may appear to be stable flooring may in fact have hidden damage.

Remember that any water will add weight to a structure. Steps must be taken to reduce water accumulation and to prevent additional water from collecting. Freezing weather may add an additional hazard in the accumulation of ice and snow. Ice might have stabilized the structure, which may become unstable when it thaws. Winds can cause collapse of structural elements, and even moderate winds are capable of toppling fire-damaged chimneys.

Figure 1.13 Perform a careful assessment of the outside of a structure before attempting to enter and determine the origin and cause of a fire. *Courtesy of Donny Howard, Yates & Associates.*

Illumination

Many incidents occur in low or poor light conditions because of time or day or location inside a large, windowless building. Providing artificial light under these circumstances is crucial to the emergency response, not only to enable ERPs to perform their jobs but also to reduce the risk of injury **(Figure 1.14)**. Many departments use floodlight units to provide exterior lighting. Although these units are extremely beneficial, the area they illuminate is generally limited to areas close to fire apparatus. Applying intensely concentrated lighting to the exterior of a building creates an adjustment problem. As an ERP emerges from the dark, smoky interior of a structure, the intense outside illumination can be temporarily blinding. ERPs should know of this effect and exercise caution to avoid tripping over obstructions such as hoselines and fallen debris.

When interior lighting is necessary, it is usually best provided by using portable lights powered by a generator. Power cords for these units must have proper insulation and highly visible colors such as yellow or orange. To avoid introducing unnecessary tripping hazards, use logic when setting up power cords to floodlights and other electric-powered equipment.

ERPs should also carry reliable battery-operated flashlights for interior illumination. Flashlights increase safety when responders are working inside a dark or smoky facility. Even daylight operations may require a flashlight for efficiency and safety. **It is very important that flashlights be approved for use in a hazardous atmosphere.** The ERP

Figure 1.14 Artificial lighting is crucial to safe operations at a nighttime emergency scene. *Courtesy of Chris E. Mickal.*

beginning the fire origin and cause portion of the investigation should be aware of the following:

- Operate electrical generators outside the fire scene in open areas or in specially designed apparatus mounts to ensure safety as well as to avoid potential contamination of the scene.

- Check to see that all equipment is electrically grounded and protected by a ground fault circuit interrupter (GFCI).

- Refill power plant fuel tanks only when the engine is completely stopped.

- Store reserve fuel in approved cans.

- Inspect apparatus fuel storage areas at least weekly to ensure that leaks have not developed from vibrations and that dents have not occurred during routine operations.

- Remember that using gasoline-fueled generators for lighting systems will produce carbon monoxide and other exhaust gases.

Block Off or Cover Spill

Figure 1.15 Either cover fuel spills or construct barricades around them to prevent contamination of the emergency scene.

Exercise caution to avoid contaminating the fire scene with spilled or leaking fuel. Precautions should be exercised to ensure that individuals do not step in fuel spills and then walk through the scene, causing contamination **(Figure 1.15)**. The spill area should be covered or barricaded, and personnel who do step in the spill should cover or remove contaminated boots.

Ventilation

Ventilation is the process of removing an atmosphere that may be contaminated with toxic by-products of combustion. In the case of a hazardous materials incident, ventilation may serve to dilute and eventually displace toxic gases with fresh air. Dusts and fumes also pose a risk to ERPs. Proper ventilation can direct these irritants away from personnel, allowing them to better perform their assigned tasks **(Figure 1.16, p. 19)**.

Figure 1.16 Proper ventilation techniques will aid greatly in fire fighting efforts by helping to remove toxic gases.

Personal Security

If at any time ERPs feel threatened by the presence of an individual or there are any indications of hostility toward them, they should remove themselves from the area. Law enforcement officials should be contacted to remove the threatening individual in a trained manner. If weapons or drugs are found at the scene, contact a law enforcement agency for their safe removal.

Animal Control

Animals of almost any type, including dogs, cats, and more exotic animals like monkeys, ferrets, snakes, lizards, exotic birds, and insects can be encountered in residential areas. Although pets may be gentle under normal circumstances, any fire and the resulting confusion and noise will likely make them fearful and difficult to handle. Try to be as calm as possible because animals can sense fear. Wait until the animal(s) has been subdued before entering the area to continue the investigation (**Figure 1.17**).

Figure 1.17 Do not attempt to deal with a frightened animal in an atmosphere of noise and chaos. Call on animal control authorities to secure the scene.

When entering any dwelling, consider all animals as potential threats. If an animal bite punctures the skin, immediate medical treatment is necessary and the animal must be captured and impounded for rabies observation. Local municipalities or counties usually retain animal control personnel who are trained in the proper handling of these animals.

Crowd Control

As the size and scope of an incident widens from fire suppression and emergency medical attention to operations that may uncover criminal activity, crowd control becomes more essential. Although perimeters have been established for many years to ensure scene security and preserve evidence, it is important to recognize that the crowd that gathers to witness emergency operations may not be composed entirely of bystanders. Some people may be there to witness the results of their crimes or to disrupt emergency operations by interfering with the investigation or otherwise compromising procedures (**Figure 1.18, p. 20**). Law enforcement personnel should be notified to assist during all emergency operations and during any subsequent investigation to ensure the safety of all.

Utility Systems
Electricity

Emergency response personnel must be cautious at all times for the possibility of electrical hazards. Before conducting emergency operations in

Figure 1.18 Law enforcement personnel are well trained in keeping crowds at a safe distance so they do not interfere with emergency scene activities.

Figure 1.19 One way to mark off downed electrical wires is to place traffic cones around them.

an area where electrical hazards may exist, ERPs must be fully trained and qualified according to *The Electrical Safety Work Practices Standard* (29 *CFR* 1910.331 through 1910.335) to ensure that the proper personnel have disconnected the power and that it has been locked or tagged out. ERPs should consider the following precautions when dealing with electrical hazards:

• Treat all wires as "live" wires.

• Be alert to fallen electrical wires on the ground because they can energize the entire area **(Figure 1.19)**.

• Be aware that pulling electrical meters can result in a blinding or explosive electrical arc if not done properly.

• Exercise extreme caution when using all ladders around electrical hazards.

• Do not rely on rubber footwear as an insulator.

• Let only power company personnel cut electrical supply wiring.

• Do not walk in "standing water" if the electrical system is energized.

• Do not switch energized electrical equipment on or off while standing in water **(Figure 1.20 p. 21)**.

• Use only explosion-proof equipment in any area where a potential explosion hazard exists **(Figure 1.21, p. 21)**.

• Shut off electrical power at a point remote from any potential explosive atmosphere.

• Be aware that there may be more than one electrical service line or electrical power source into a structure that may not be disconnected.

Do not enter an electrical vault, substation, generator station, or transfer station before the power has been shut off (circuit opened). Always consider everything within these enclosures as being energized until confirmed by a qualified representative of the electric utility company.

Fuel Gas

A working knowledge of the hazards and correct procedures for handling incidents related to natural gas and liquefied petroleum gas (LPG) is important to every first responder. Many houses, mobile homes, and businesses use natural gas or LPG for cooking, heating, or industrial processes. ERPs must be familiar with gas distribution and usage. This knowledge will help prevent personal injury or additional damage caused by these gases.

NOTE: Consult NFPA 54, *National Fuel Gas Code*, for additional information.

Figure 1.20 Follow all safety procedures when switching off energized equipment.

Figure 1.21 Remember that using an ordinary telephone -- or cell phone -- in a hazardous atmosphere can be very dangerous. Make sure that any phones used are explosion-proof like the one shown. *Courtesy of Tim Stemple.*

Water

Although water is not usually considered a safety problem for ERPs, water leaking from broken pipes, sprinkler systems, or disrupted underground mains can create major safety concerns. The addition of the resulting "dead load" to an already-weakened structure can cause an unexpected collapse resulting in injury or death even hours after the initial fire or explosion. Another major concern is the collection of water in basements or low spaces in and near the incident site. Because these hazards, which include open wells and cisterns, can be difficult to detect, they represent a significant falling or drowning danger. To guard against such an event, the water utility should be notified and a request made to cut service to the incident site. Drain chutes and catchalls can be constructed with salvage covers to divert or retain water as needed. Water can be pumped out of basements, but it is not recommended that fire service pumps be used for this purpose. Hazardous areas should be marked off or barricaded to prevent ERPs from falling and becoming injured.

Sewage/Drainage

Some incidents may compromise the sanitary or storm sewer systems. Large quantities of wastewater can contribute to the dead load being supported by the structure. As with water utilities, this situation can lead to a structural failure and collapse. Aside from the possibility of collapse and drowning, the added concern of contamination and disease must be considered. The sewer utility and the local public health officer must be notified when situations of this type are found. Care must also be taken when working in a rural environment, where it is necessary to take precautions when working around cesspools, farm manure, or drainage ditches. These locations should be cordoned off using scene or biological hazard tape **(Figure 1.22, p. 22)**.

Legal Issues

The safety issues covered in this chapter are not merely recommendations. Many of these practices are mandated by government occupational health and safety regulations and may carry such penalties for their breach as fines, imprisonment, and/or

Figure 1.22 Ditches, cesspools, wells, and other open areas can be very hazardous, especially at night. Be sure to cordon off any such areas or openings like this drainage ditch to prevent injuries.

exposure to civil liability. Many of the NFPA standards, such as NFPA 704 or 1500, may be adopted by reference, changing their requirements from recommendations to legal mandates.

Summary

When conducting emergency scene operations, personal safety is of primary importance. ERPs must be vigilant in the recognition and identification of potential safety and health hazards. A scene analysis determines the level of personal protective equipment necessary to safely begin the origin and cause determination. Compromising safety to overcome either inconvenience (such as the lack of protective equipment) or discomfort (such as wearing an SCBA or other respirator) should not be an option. It is essential that all personnel involved with operations at the emergency scene work within the Incident Management System and stay within a direct chain of command. All established health and safety guidelines must be followed.

Scene security and structural integrity must also be established and maintained to ensure a safe environment for ERPs. Atmospheric testing for toxic gases and the possibility that the atmosphere is oxygen deficient are other safety precautions

that should be taken. Structural ventilation may be used to assist in countering either of these conditions, and atmospheric monitoring must be used to evaluate the results. PPE can then be selected based upon the findings of scene risk evaluation and atmospheric monitoring. Once inside, other safety considerations include electrical hazards, dark or poorly illuminated areas, animals not yet removed from the area, the possibility of infectious diseases, and hazardous materials (including the possibility of clandestine drug labs and other illegal activities). ERPs must continually be aware of the inherently dangerous conditions that may pose a threat to their health and safety. These include a terrorist attack or secondary devices involving explosives, biological agents, and weapons of mass destruction.

Chapter 2:
The Roles of Those Involved with Fire and Explosion Investigations

Job Performance Requirements

This chapter provides information that will assist the reader in meeting the following performance requirements from NFPA 1001, *Fire Fighter Professional Qualifications*, 2002 edition and NFPA 1021, *Standard for Fire Officer Professional Qualifications*, 2003 edition. Boldfaced portions of the standard are specifically addressed in this chapter.

NFPA 1001

Chapter 5 Fire Fighter I

Chapter 5.3 Fireground Operations

5.3.8* Extinguish fires in exterior Class A materials, given fires in stacked or piled and small unattached structures or storage containers that can be fought from the exterior, attack lines, hand tools and master stream devices, and an assignment, so that exposures are protected, the spread of fire is stopped, collapse hazards are avoided, water application is effective, the fire is extinguished, and **signs of the origin area(s) and arson are preserved.**

(A) **Requisite Knowledge.** Types of attack lines and water streams appropriate for attacking stacked, piled materials and outdoor fires; dangers — such as collapse — associated with stacked and piled materials; various extinguishing agents and their effect on different material configurations; tools and methods to use in breaking up various types of materials; the difficulties related to complete extinguishment of stacked and piled materials; water application methods for exposure protection and fire extinguishment; dangers such as exposure to toxic or hazardous materials associated with storage building and container fires; **obvious signs of origin and cause; and techniques for the preservation of fire cause evidence.**

(B) **Requisite Skills** The ability to recognize inherent hazards related to the material's configuration, operate handlines or master streams, break up material using hand tools and water streams, evaluate for complete extinguishment, operate hose lines and other water application devices, evaluate and modify water application for maximum penetration, search for and expose hidden fires, **assess patterns for origin determination, and evaluate for complete extinguishment.**

5.3.13 Overhaul a fire scene, given personal protective equipment, attack line, hand tools, a flashlight, and an assignment, so that structural integrity is not compromised, **all hidden fires are discovered, fire cause evidence is preserved, and the fire is extinguished.**

(A) **Requisite Knowledge.** Types of fire attack lines and water application devices most effective for overhaul, water application methods for extinguishment that limit water damage, types of tools and methods used to expose hidden fire, dangers associated with overhaul, **obvious signs of area of origin or signs of arson, and reasons for protection of fire scene.**

(B) **Requisite Skills.** The ability to deploy and operate an attack line; remove flooring, ceiling, and wall components to expose void spaces without compromising structural integrity; apply water for maximum effectiveness; expose and extinguish hidden fires in walls, ceilings, and subfloor spaces; recognize and **preserve obvious signs of area of origin and arson; and evaluate for complete extinguishment.**

NFPA 1021

Chapter 4 Fire Officer I

4.5* Inspection and Investigation

4.5.1 Evaluate available information, given a fire incident, observations, and interviews of first-arriving members and other individuals involved in the incident, so that a preliminary cause of the fire is determined, reports are completed, and, if required, **the scene is secured and all pertinent information is turned over to an investigator.**

(A) **Requisite Knowledge.** Common causes of fire, fire growth and development, **and policies and procedures for calling for investigators.**

(B) **Requisite Skills. The ability to** determine basic fire cause, **conduct interviews, and write reports.**

4.5.2 Secure an incident scene, given rope or barrier tape, so that unauthorized persons can recognize the perimeters of the scene and are kept from restricted areas, and all evidence or potential evidence is protected from damage or destruction.

(A) **Requisite Knowledge. Types of evidence, the importance of fire scene security, and evidence preservation.**

(B) **Requisite Skills. The ability to establish perimeters at an incident scene.**

NFPA 1021

Chapter 6 Fire Fighter II

6.2 Fire Department Communications

6.2.1 Complete a basic incident report, given the report forms, guidelines, and information, so that all pertinent information is recorded, the information is accurate, and the report is complete.

(A) **Requisite Knowledge.** Content requirements for basic incident reports, **the purpose and usefulness of accurate reports, consequences of inaccurate reports, how to obtain necessary information,** and required coding procedures.

6.3 Fireground Operations

6.3.4* Protect evidence of fire cause and origin, given a flashlight and overhaul tools, so that the evidence is noted and protected from further disturbance until investigators can arrive on the scene.

(A) **Requisite Knowledge.** Methods to assess origin and cause; types of evidence; means to protect various types of evidence; **the role and relationship of Fire Fighter IIs, criminal investigators, and insurance investigators in fire investigations; and the effects and problems associated with removing property or evidence from the scene.**

Chapter 2
The Roles of Those Involved with Fire and Explosion Investigations

It is the responsibility of the fire department to respond to and extinguish a fire as quickly as possible. However, fire suppression, salvage, and overhaul activities often impair the ability of the fire investigator to determine the fire's origin and cause by altering or obliterating evidence. Often, actions taken by the fire department to bring a fire under control may unintentionally contaminate or move evidence from its original location, diminishing its value to the person conducting the investigation **(Figure 2.1)**. Destroying, losing, or altering evidence, whether intentional or unintentional, is known as *spoliation*. It is the responsibility of all ERPs to avoid spoliating evidence or potential evidence as much as possible. ERPs must be aware that spoliation can result in monetary sanctions, dismissal of a defense or claim, exclusion of expert testimony, and prosecution under statutes relating to obstruction of justice.

Figure 2.1 Although it can be difficult to remember during an emergency, firefighters need to remain aware that the actions taken during fire suppression efforts can obscure or destroy potential evidence. *Courtesy of Donny Howard, Yates & Associates.*

NOTE: Spoliation is discussed in more detail in Chapter 7 of this manual.

> It is extremely important that all emergency response personnel, whether firefighters, emergency medical workers, or law enforcement officers, take precautions to preserve evidence during initial emergency scene operations.

Information gathered at the scene is of critical importance to the success of the investigation. Legal proceedings concerning a particular fire may become necessary, and for these reasons, ERP should be responsible for gathering information relevant to the origin and cause of the fire. Whether the ERP makes the cause determination, or that responsibility is passed to a qualified investigator, the ERP should observe, document, and preserve as much information as possible **(Figure 2.2, p. 26)**. This process is critical in reconstructing the scene and in making an accurate determination of the cause of the fire.

This chapter details the responsibilities of the ERP in the process of determining the fire origin and cause and in preserving evidentiary materials for the fire and explosion investigator. The roles of other sources of assistance outside the fire department -- law enforcement, insurance companies, private corporations, and governmental agencies -- are also explained. This chapter highlights observations the responding ERP should make while approaching the scene, upon arrival, during fire

Figure 2.2 Carefully handling potential evidence will make the job of determining fire origin and cause easier. *Courtesy of Donny Howard, Yates & Associates.*

fighting operations, and during mitigation of the incident. The procedures for properly securing the fire scene and for preserving of evidence are also discussed. The chapter concludes with an overview of legal issues pertaining to fire cause determination and investigation and an annotated bibliography of additional resources.

Responsibilities of Emergency Response Personnel

At one time, emergency fire response was limited to just one agency: the fire department. With changing times, a more proactive approach has been adopted by many communities with regard to which ERPs are automatically dispatched to emergencies. The traditional fire department response contingent has been supplemented with emergency medical personnel, law enforcement agencies, and sometimes other diverse groups. Each is included as part of an integrated response team resulting in a very positive effect upon the delivery of emergency services.

There are no single rules for the coordination of investigative efforts at the emergency scene. In some areas, police and fire department personnel respond to every fire call. In other areas, the incident commander is responsible for calling law enforcement as needed for scene control and investigative assistance. It is critical that ERPs be aware of the guidelines and/or regulations in their areas for contacting law enforcement personnel, calling in fire investiga-

tors, and following guidelines in all matters relating to legal issues. Regulations and guidelines will vary depending on the authority having jurisdiction. It is imperative that ERPs always take appropriate steps to ensure the protection of possible evidence.

NOTE: Proper techniques respecting identification and preservation of evidence are discussed in Chapter 7, Preserving Physical Fire Scene Evidence.

Due to their location at the time of dispatch, any emergency response agency may be the "first in" unit at the fire scene. By their nature, emergency scenes often call for the services of several agencies **(Figure 2.3)**. For example, what begins as a fire call can quickly shift to a fire/law enforcement/EMS incident. This dynamic is also very common with emergency medical responses. A request for help for a burn victim may turn out to be a working fire, a crime scene, a hazardous material exposure, or even an explosion.

Figures 2.3 a and b The services of multiple emergency agencies may be needed to mitigate the fire, treat victims, or preserve scene evidence. *A courtesy of Chris E. Mickal. B courtesy of CT Office of State Fire Marshal.*

Determining the cause of a fire may be a relatively simple procedure that requires only the expertise of the ERP. More complex fire incidents or possible crime scenes often require the additional assistance of law enforcement personnel and qualified fire investigators at the local, state or provincial, and federal level. The guidelines for initiating each of these steps vary among jurisdictions and according to the nature of the incident.

 In the event of a fatality, the emergency scene should be treated as a crime scene and proper authorities contacted immediately.

Initial Observations

Even as they approach the scene, ERPs should observe and note conditions and other activities that might be related to the incident, including location and size of the fire, smoke conditions, witnesses, and unusual human behavior. An accurate initial report must be transmitted to the dispatching authority, identifying the unit or designation, a description of the situation as it is at that moment, and the declaration of Command. The following situations should be noted. Evaluating each condition or situation is important to ensure the safety of all ERPs as well as to assist in successful origin and cause determination:

- Size and location of fire on arrival.

- Doors and windows, open or closed; signs of forced entry prior to fire suppression entry.

- Tools, such as pry bars and screwdrivers, found in unusual areas may have been used so that someone could gain entry facility and set a fire (**Figure 2.4**).

- Any modifications made to normal egress that would hamper the efforts of the fire department to enter the structure or to conduct suppression activities (**Figure 2.5**)

- Any obstructions blocking the view and thereby delaying detection of the fire.

- Metal cans or plastic containers found inside or outside the structure may have been used to transport liquid accelerants (**Figure 2.6**).

- Familiar faces in the crowd of bystanders. They may be fire buffs or they may be habitual firesetters.

- Any vehicles or persons leaving the scene.

Figure 2.4 Look for common burglary tools, such as screwdrivers and pry bars, near the openings of a structure.

Figure 2.5 Furniture that has been placed to block the entrance to a structure is a sign of potential suspicious activity and should be noted.

Figure 2.6. Containers that can be used to transport flammable liquids should be noted and photographed if they are found in an unlikely location.

On-Scene Report

An on-scene report provides a record of the incident and fixes the time, place, and situation as found. Additionally, the on-scene report clearly establishes a visible commander on the scene. In the early stages of an incident, this individual has the responsibility for identifying the type of emergency, establishing a course of action, and beginning the process of preserving a record for later review. To accomplish this effectively, the ERP must begin to make mental notes of the situation as it is upon arrival. In addition to making an initial report, the ERP should take note of the presence, location, and condition of physical evidence as well as the identity of any victims or witnesses.

Vehicles at the Scene

The location of parked vehicles or vehicles seen leaving the incident may lead to additional witnesses or other persons of interest who may be involved with the incident. When noting vehicles, the ERP should remember where a vehicle was parked, how it was facing, and where it was located relative to the incident. Vehicles that are observed leaving the scene should be noted for model, color, type, direction of travel, excessive speed, erratic driving, and any description of the operator or passengers. If possible, a license number and any other distinguishing features should be noted. If ERP consistently see the same vehicles and/or persons at multiple fire incidents, investigators should be notified immediately and the information passed along.

Observations about the Fire

Emergency response personnel should determine the general location of the fire, its size, flame height, and make an estimate of its intensity. As with flames, observations about the location, movement, and volume of smoke may also be important. Unusual color of smoke or flame may also be noteworthy.

Wind

Also to be remembered is the direction and velocity of the wind. Windy conditions will drive the smoke and flames with it, feeding oxygen to the fire. It is very important to look for broken windows, open doors, or other openings that allow wind to assist in the growth of the fire. A wind fed, oxygen-enriched fire is a dynamic, catastrophic event for a structure. A small fire can suddenly "blow up" and grow at an almost unbelievable rate. It poses an immediate safety concern for all ERPs because the incident structure and adjacent structures can become quickly engulfed (**Figure 2.7**).

Figure 2.7 Windy conditions can cause fire to spread quickly to adjacent structures. *Courtesy of Chris E. Mickal.*

Type and Condition of Occupancy

A determination of the type of occupancy and its use must be made. Is this a single family dwelling being used as business, or is it a storage facility housing a manufacturing or chemical processing site? Deviation from the standard type of use for a structure may indicate the presence of additional hazards, possible illegal activities, or simply a nontraditional business setting.

Observations During Suppression Operations

Once fire suppression activities have begun, the techniques that are employed by the fire department should be either observed or noted down because they are critical to the post-suppression fire scene. The points of access that are used by ERPs should be noted as well as the method used to make entry. The size of hoselines that are deployed and the stream pattern selected are important when determining the extent to which the scene has been disrupted by suppression activities. Ventilation can also have an effect on the ability to determine origin and cause. Actions taken by fire suppression forces to secure utilities are also significant. The condition of the gas meter, electric meter, or breaker panel should be documented.

Likewise, the condition of an intrusion system or fire protection system, if present, should be noted. Deficiencies that may have affected their operation should be noted **(Figure 2.8)**. These deficiencies include shut or partially closed valves, alarms in a trouble mode or disconnected, and lack of current inspection and maintenance records.

Figure 2.8 The battery was disconnected from this alarm before an intentional fire was set. *Courtesy of Donny Howard, Yates & Associates.*

The presence of any security recorders and their location relative to the incident should be noted and the recorded data should be secured and preserved for later review. Neighboring security systems or in-car camera recordings from other

emergency response vehicles may also provide an accurate record of the incident and its cause **(Figure 2.9)**.

Figure 2.9 Information from security videotapes may be of great benefit to fire investigators.

Responsibilities After the Fire

After the fire, the ERP should interview occupants, owners, and witnesses to obtain information for use in the fire investigation report. In accordance with local policy, the ERP then conducts the preliminary origin and cause investigation. As soon as possible, the ERP should speak to other ERPs to obtain all facts concerning the incident that may be relevant to the origin and cause determination. If possible, it should be requested that salvage and overhaul work be delayed until the area of origin and cause has been determined.

Salvage and overhaul should be performed very carefully. Debris should not be moved any more than necessary, especially in the area of origin, because it may hamper the investigation **(Figure 2.10)**. It is recommended that the ERP responsible for the origin and cause investigation observe any salvage and overhaul operations.

Conduct at the Scene

While conducting an initial inquiry, the ERP should allow the owners or occupants of the property to talk freely if they are inclined to do so. Give them a sympathetic ear. Some valuable information is often gathered this way.

It is very important that ERPs never make statements of accusation, personal opinion, or probable cause to anyone. Careless joking and unauthorized or premature remarks that are published or broadcast can be very embarrassing to all of the agencies represented at the scene. A sufficient reply to any question concerning the fire cause should be, "The fire is under investigation."

In the event the responsibility for cause determination is transferred to a fire investigator, ERPs should make their statements only to the investigator. Any public statement regarding the fire cause should be made only after the investigator and ranking fire officer have agreed to its accuracy and validity and have given permission for it to be released.

Securing the Incident Scene

The most efficient and complete efforts to determine the cause of a fire are wasted unless the scene and evidence are properly secured and guarded until the fire scene investigation has been completed. The emergency response agency, usually the fire department, should keep control of the premises and guard the scene until all evidence has been identified, documented, and collected **(Figure 2.11, p 31)**.

Figure 2.10 Once debris from a fire has been thrown away, its value in the investigative process is severely lessened. ERPs may need to supervise overhaul efforts before contents can be removed. *Courtesy of Donny Howard, Yates & Associates.*

Figure 2.11 Emergency services personnel must maintain physical control of an emergency scene until all fire origin and cause evidence has been collected.

ERPs with responsibility for investigation should consult with their local jurisdiction's legal authorities regarding their rights of entry and investigation on the property.

Access to the scene should be limited to individuals whose presence is absolutely necessary. All individuals, including emergency personnel, who are granted access to the scene by the incident commander should be escorted and their presence documented in a scene entry log (**Figure 2.12, p 32**).

Cordoning off the area can also help provide a safe and secure fire scene. With the area cordoned, bystanders are kept at a safe distance from the incident and out of the way of emergency personnel. There are no specific boundaries for the cordon. Cordoning can be accomplished with rope or specially designed fire and police line tape. It may be attached to signs, utility poles, parking meters, vehicles, or any other objects readily available. Once cordoning is in place, law enforcement personnel should be requested to monitor the barriers to make sure that people do not cross the line (**Figures 2.13 a and b**).

Figures 2.13 a and b Areas under investigation need to be cordoned off to keep the scene secure and to preserve evidence. *Both photos courtesy of Donny Howard, Yates & Associates.*

Responsibilities of the Fire Department Company Officer

It is necessary for the company officer and all other ERPs to work together to determine the cause of the fire. If their joint efforts cannot determine the origin and cause of the fire, a trained fire and explosion investigator should be called immediately. The fire department should have guidelines that establish the criteria for calling a fire investigator. Calling for an investigator does not imply that the fire was deliberately set -- it implies only that the ERPs need assistance in determining the cause. An officer who knows when to call for an investigator is fulfilling his or her duties as a professional company officer. The fire officer or ERP who accompanies the fire and explosives investigator will gain valuable experience. This will help to build an experience base as well as to foster a good working relationship with local fire and explosion investigators (**Figure 2.14, p. 33**).

FIRE SCENE ENTRY LOG INCIDENT # _____ LOCATION _____

Date	Time In	Time Out	Name	Agency	Purpose of Entry	Accompanied By

Figure 2.12 A scene entry log is useful for keeping track of individuals who enter and leave the emergency scene. This information may be essential for legal purposes.

Figure 2.14 All emergency personnel, from the first-in firefighter to the fire investigator, must learn to work together efficiently.

Participation of the Insurance Industry

Municipalities, whether large or small, have limits as to the time, personnel, and resources that can be expended on a fire cause investigation. Valuable time and resources can be saved through cooperative efforts between the ERPs and the insurance company for the property involved. Although ERPs can legally cooperate with an insurance company, they may not direct the insurance company's own investigation -- and vice versa. However, the fire department and the insurance company may exchange information if they follow proper legal guidelines and document such exchanges. When working with an insurance company investigator, ERPs must still perform the origin and cause determination in an independent manner.

Roles of Individuals Associated with the Insurance Industry

Insurance Adjuster

Insurance company adjusters are employed by an insurance company or are independent adjusters retained by an insurance company as its representative. The insurance adjuster's responsibility is usually to visit the incident site, collect police and fire reports, create diagrams, interview witnesses, and take photos of the scene on the insurer's behalf. Insurance adjusters may, upon notification of a loss, contract the services of specialized fire and arson investigators, bringing their expertise into the investigation. This investigation, even though it is often made simultaneously with law enforcement/fire investigations, remains independent. It is not uncommon for each group to compare their findings and hypotheses of origin and cause. Care must always be exercised to ensure the impartiality of each report. Contradictory conclusions usually result from differing investigative methodologies or in some instances are due to an oversight by one team of investigators.

Public Claims Adjuster

A public adjuster is a person retained by the insured (not the insurance company), to establish the scope and the value of the loss.

Special Investigation Unit

Some insurance companies have special investigation units (SIUs) to investigate fraud, or large or complex losses. Sometimes a member of the special investigation unit also becomes involved on the insurer's behalf in investigating the cause of the fire. This may include retaining law firms, private fire investigation firms, engineers, or other specialized resources.

Other Resources
Private Fire Investigators

The persons or companies affected by the fire may conduct a separate investigation utilizing private fire investigators, engineers, law firms, and other experts. Examples of such interested parties may include the victim of the fire, and manufacturers or distributors of products that are suspected of causing or contributing to the spread of the fire. Cooperation between the fire department and representatives of these other interested parties may provide for savings in time and resources to all concerned. It should be remembered that ERPs have an obligation to avoid any undue influence on their findings by these representatives. The investigation must be free of bias and corroborated by scientific principles within the ERP's level of expertise.

State and Federal Agencies

Federal, state or provincial governments often provide fire and explosion investigation assistance to local governmental agencies. In the United States, this assistance may be provided through a law enforcement agency such as the state police, by the state fire marshal's office, or by the state insurance commission. The federal government provides assistance through the Department of Justice (DOJ) and the Department of Homeland Security (DHS). In Canada, assistance may be provided by provincial police departments, the Royal Canadian Mounted Police (RCMP, a federal police agency), or by provincial fire commissioners' or marshal's offices.

Utility Companies

Utility companies can also provide valuable assistance following an incident, which may continue through the origin and cause determination. Utility company representatives can provide experienced technicians to assist the ERP during the investigation by identifying and testing equipment. Gas and electric companies may test for faults within their system, which may assist in establishing the fire origin. One must be cautious, however, about the possibility that the utility company has an interest in the loss, for example, where an allegation that the company was at fault might arise. As with other interested parties who are involved in the investigation, the ERP should be careful to conduct an independent investigation.

Legal Considerations

As in every field, the law in the field of fire investigation is not static. It changes constantly and varies from state to state and province to province. ERPs must be familiar with the most common legal issues that are encountered during a fire investigation. Their actions or lack of action can have serious consequences to the fire investigation and any subsequent legal or criminal issues:

- **Right of Entry**: When responding to an emergency, ERPs have the right to enter and remain upon the subject premises. They have the continued right to remain on the scene while dealing with the emergency. Once control of the scene has been relinquished, however, ERPs can re-enter the scene only after they have secured permission from the owner/occupant or have obtained a court-authorized warrant.

- **Search and Seizure**: A scene investigation is by its nature a search in legal terms. A person must have the right of entry to search property, either as part of mitigating an emergency, with the consent of the owner or occupant, or with a warrant. In order to remove property that may be relevant to a fire origin and cause investigation, the ERP will require either consent of the owner or a court-authorized warrant. In Canada, after an emergency has ended, either a warrant or legislative authority is required to search or seize property.

- **Statements and the Miranda Warning**: If a fire investigation turns into a criminal investigation and an individual becomes the focus of the investigation, the individual must be advised of his or her constitutional rights before an interview can be conducted or the individual is placed in custody. It is incumbent on the ERP to recognize if and when an investigation may involve a crime. ERPs should then obtain direction from a law enforcement official before proceeding.

- **Chain of Custody and continuity of evidence**: Evidence taken from a fire scene is required to be documented and a chain of custody developed and maintained to ensure the integrity of the evidence.

- **Spoliation**: NFPA 921 defines spoliation as, "Loss, destruction or material alteration of a object or document that is evidence or potential evidence in a legal proceeding, by one who has the responsibility for its preservation." Courts have fashioned a variety of remedies that can have a severe effect on the admissibility of evidence or the outcome of any litigation that arises from the fire.

NOTE: Refer to **Appendix B, Federal Constitutional Search and Seizure Issues in Fire Scene Investigations** for more information.

Because ERPs may be called to testify in court, it is imperative that they consult their own local resources on legal issues to establish proper guidelines and procedures. Individuals such as the jurisdictional attorney or the local prosecuting attorney will be able to provide the necessary guidance. For further information on legal issues relating to fire investigations, see the following:

- NFPA 921, 2004 edition, Chapter 11, "Legal Considerations."

- IFSTA's Fire Investigator manual, 1st ed., Chapter 16, "Presenting Investigative Findings," and Appendix B.

- National Fire Academy (NFA) "Courtroom Preparation and Testimony for First Responders" course

Summary

The responding firefighters at the fire scene are the first to observe the important details of the behavior of the fire and conditions in the area. The company officer continues observations at the scene and interviews witnesses, owners, firefighters, and others.

Observations noted en route, upon arrival, and during and after fire fighting efforts can give ERP important information. ERPs and any subsequent fire investigators must also protect and preserve evidence and document the entire investigation process. This is done so that evidence can be used to properly determine the origin and cause of the fire or to assign responsibility. The combined efforts of ERP contribute to a proper fire cause determination investigation. If a fire cause cannot be determined, an investigator should be called for further assistance.

Because this is an introductory text, the reader is referred to the following publications and standards for more in-depth information:

- Fire Protection Publications, *Safety and Health Guidelines for Fire and Explosion Investigators*, Michael L. Donahue
  — Fire and explosion safety practices
  — Investigative sources of information
  — Potential safety and health hazards

- IFSTA, **Essentials of Fire Fighting,** 4th Edition
  — Fire behavior (combustion, special considerations, classification of fires, products of combustion, etc.)
  — Protecting evidence for fire cause determination

- IFSTA **Respiratory Protection for Fire and Emergency Services**, 1st Edition
  — Use of respiratory protective equipment on an emergency scene, including investigations

- IFSTA **Fire Department Safety Officer**, 1st Edition
  — Health hazards in a particular facility
  — Scene safety and PPE
  — Post-incident analyses and reports

- IFSTA **Wildland Fire Fighting for Structural Firefighters**, 4th Edition
  — Fire prevention and investigation of wildland fires

- **Kirk's Fire Investigation,** 5th Edition
  — Chemistry of combustion (elements, compounds, and their reactions)
  — Nature and behavior of fire
  — Combustion properties of various fuel sources
  — Structure and wildland fire investigations
  — Electrical causes of fire
  — Laboratory sciences (identification of volatile accelerants, chemical incendiaries, etc.)

- NFPA 921, *Guide for Fire and Explosion Investigations*
  — Basic methods of fire investigation
  — Products of combustion and fire development (basic chemistry of combustion)
  — Detailed breakdown of fire patterns and what to look for
  — The roles that electricity and fuel gas play in a building fire
  — Planning and documenting the investigation
  — Identifying, preserving, and examining physical evidence
  — Analyzing the cause of the fire or explosion
  — Special concerns with wildland fires

- NFPA 1001, Standard for Fire Fighter Professional Qualifications
  — Qualifications for Firefighter I and Firefighter II certification
  — Fireground operations and communications, rescue operations, prevention, preparedness, and maintenance

- NFPA 1033, *Standard for Professional Qualifications for Fire Investigator*
  — Basic duties associated with fire investigation such as sizing up the scene, collecting evidence, and documentation of the investigation

- NFPA 1250, *Recommended Practice in Emergency Service Organization Risk Management*
  — Identifying and analyzing risk exposures
  — General procedures and alternatives for risk management

- NFPA 1401, *Recommended Practice for Fire Service Training Reports and Records*
  — General information on the maintenance, record keeping, and evaluation of a training program

- NFPA 1404, *Standard for Fire Service Respiratory Protection Training*
  — Information on the development of a respiratory protection training program
  — Basics on inspection of respiratory protection equipment

- NFPA 1500, *Standard on Fire Department Occupational Safety and Health Program*
  — Safety issues related to PPE and safety during emergency operations

- NFPA 1521, *Standard for Fire Department Safety Officer*
  — Responsibilities and qualifications for Health and Safety Officer as well as the Incident Safety Officer
  — Several ISO functions are examined, such as incident management, fire suppression, and accident investigations

- NFPA 1561, *Standard on Emergency Services Incident Management System*
  — Similar to NFPA 1521 with the addition of accountability issues for scene resources
  — System components for an emergency incident management system

- NFPA 1851, *Standard on Selection, Care, and Maintenance of Structural Fire Fighting Protective Ensembles*
  — Maintenance and care of fire fighting clothing (cleaning, repairs, etc.)

- NFPA 1852, *Standard on Selection, Care, and Maintenance of Open-Circuit SCBA*
  — Taking care of a SCBA (proper use, cleaning, and general maintenance)

- NFPA 1982, *Standard on Personal Alert Safety Systems (PASS)*
  — Personal Alert Safety Systems (PASS) specifications

- NFPA 1991, *Standard on Vapor-Protective Ensembles for Hazardous Materials Emergencies*
  — Vapor-protective ensemble specifications for hazardous materials emergencies (design, performance, and test requirements/methods)

- NFPA 1992, *Standard on Liquid Splash-Protective Ensembles and Clothing for Hazardous Materials Emergencies*
  — Liquid splash-protective ensemble specifications for hazardous materials emergencies (design, performance, and test requirements)

- NFPA 1994, *Standard on Protective Ensembles for Chemical/Biological Terrorism Incidents*
  — Protective ensemble specifications for chemical/biological terrorism incidents (design, performance, and test requirements)

- NFPA 1999, *Standard on Protective Clothing for Emergency Medical Operations*
  — Protective clothing specifications for emergency medical operations (design, performance, and test requirements)

Chapter 3:
Fire Behavior

Courtesy of Donny Howard, Yates & Associates.

Convection

Convection is the transfer of heat energy by the movement of fluids (liquids or gases.) As a fire begins to grow, the hot air and products of combustion rise. If you hold your hand over a flame, you are able to feel the heat even though your hand is not in direct contact with the flame. The heat is transferred to your hand by convection. **(Figure 3.3)** When heat is transferred by convection, there is movement or circulation of a fluid from one place to another.

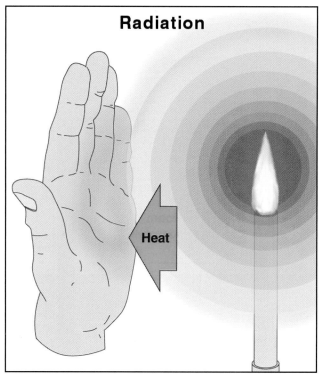

Figure 3.4 Radiation is the transmission of energy as an electromagnetic wave without an intervening medium.

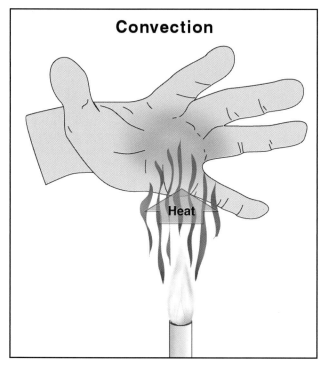

Figure 3.3 Convection is the transfer of heat energy by the movement of heated liquids or gases.

Radiation

Thermal radiation is the heat transfer by way of electromagnetic waves. If you hold your hand near to the side of the small fire used as an example in the preceding section, you would also be able to feel heat. This heat reaches your hand by radiation. Radiation does not require an intervening medium **(Figure 3.4)**. Because it is electromagnetic waves, the energy travels in a straight line at the speed of light (186,000 miles/sec). All warm objects radiate heat. The best example of heat transfer by radiation is the sun's heat. The energy travels at the speed of light from the sun through space (a vacuum) and warms the earth's surface. Radiation is the pre-

dominant heat transfer mechanism of most exposure fires (fires ignited in fuel packages or buildings that are remote from the fuel package or building of origin). As a fire grows, energy is radiated from it in the form of heat. In large fires it is possible for the radiated heat to cause ignition of buildings or other fuel packages some distance away **(Figure 3.5)**. Radiation may ultimately lead to flashover in compartment fires. Heat energy transmitted by radiation travels through vacuums and substantial air spaces that would normally disrupt conduction and convection.

Chemical Reactions

Before discussing combustion and fire growth, it is important to understand the concept of chemical reactions. Whenever two or more substances combine to form a third substance, chemists describe the transformation as a chemical reaction. Matter is transformed from one state to another or a new substance is produced. The simplest of these reactions occurs when matter changes state, which is called a physical change. In a physical change, the chemical makeup of the substance is not altered. The change of state that occurs when water freezes is a physical change **(Figure 3.6)**.

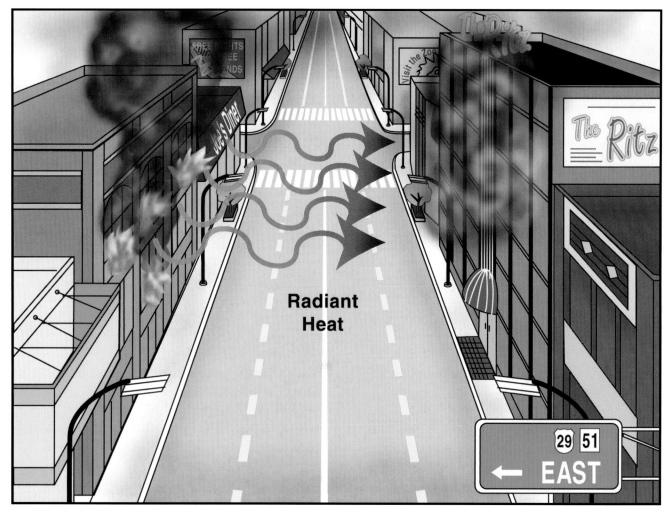

Figure 3.5 Radiated heat is one of the major sources of fire spread to exposures.

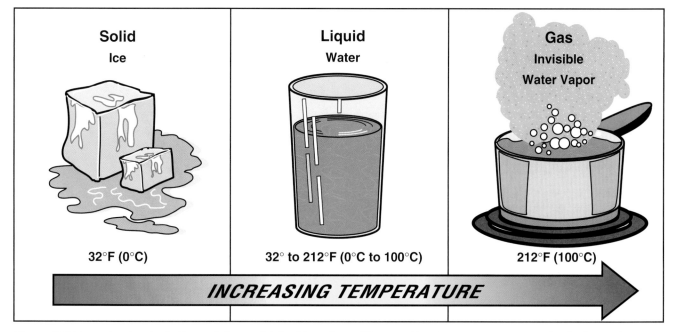

Figure 3.6 Example of water in three states: solid, liquid, and gas. The transition from one state to another is due to the increase or decrease of the temperature of the water.

A more complex reaction occurs when substances are transformed into new substances with different chemical and possibly physical properties. These changes are defined as chemical changes. The change that occurs when hydrogen and oxygen are combined to form water is a chemical change. In this case, the chemical and physical properties of the materials being combined are altered. Two materials that are normally gases at room temperature are converted into a substance that is a clear liquid at room temperature.

Chemical and physical changes almost always involve an exchange of energy. Reactions that give off energy as they occur are called exothermic. Reactions that absorb energy as they occur are called endothermic. When fuels are burned in air, the fuel vapors chemically react with the oxygen in the air, and both heat and light energies are released in an exothermic reaction. Water changing state from liquid to gas (steam) requires the input of energy, thus the conversion is endothermic.

One of the more common chemical reactions is oxidation (**Figure 3.7**). Oxidation is the formation of a chemical bond between oxygen and another element. Oxygen is one of the more common elements on earth (our atmosphere is composed of 21 percent oxygen) and reacts with almost every other element found on the planet. The oxidation reaction releases energy or is exothermic. The most familiar example of an oxidation reaction is rusting of iron. The combination of oxygen and iron produces a flaky red compound called iron oxide or more commonly, rust. Because this is an exothermic process, it always produces heat. Usually the process is very slow, and the heat dissipates before it is noticed. Fire is an example of a rapid oxidation process where light and heat are emitted and are not harmlessly dissipated.

Combustion

Fire and combustion are terms that are often used interchangeably. Technically, however, fire is a form of combustion. Combustion is a chemical reaction that is a self-sustaining process of rapid oxidation of a fuel that produces heat and light. Combustion is an exothermic reaction; fire is a rapid oxidation of combustible materials accompanied by a release of energy in the form of heat and light. The time it

Figure 3.7 The most familiar example of an oxidation reaction is rusting of iron.

takes a reaction to occur is the determining factor in the type of reaction that is observed. At the very slow end of the time spectrum is oxidation, where the reaction is too slow to be observed. At the upper end of the spectrum are explosions that result from the very rapid reaction of a fuel and an oxidizer. In these cases, a large amount of energy is released over a very short period of time (**Figure 3.8**).

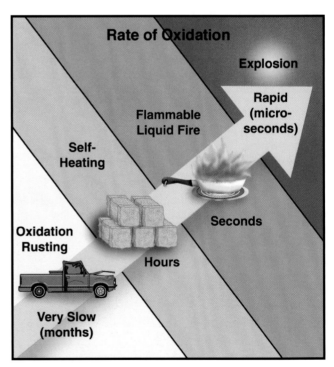

Figure 3.8 Combustion, a self-sustaining chemical reaction, may be very slow or very rapid.

Fire Tetrahedron

For many years the fire triangle (oxygen, fuel, and heat) was used to teach the components of fire. While this simple example is useful, it is not technically correct. There are four components necessary for combustion to occur:

- Oxygen (oxidizing agent)
- Fuel (reducing agent)
- Heat
- Self-sustained chemical reaction

These components can be graphically described as the fire tetrahedron **(Figure 3.9)**. Each component of the tetrahedron must be in place for combustion to occur. This concept is extremely important to students of fire suppression, prevention, and investigation. Remove any one of the four components, and combustion will not occur. If ignition has already occurred, the fire is extinguished when one of the components is removed from the reaction. To better understand fire and its behavior, each of the components of the tetrahedron is discussed in the following sections.

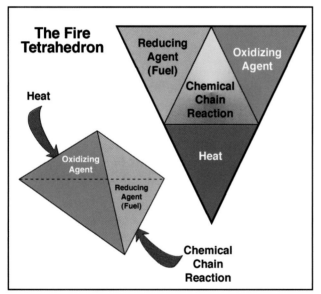

Figure 3.9 The components of the fire tetrahedron.

Oxidizing Agent

Oxidizing agents are those materials that yield oxygen or other oxidizing gases during the course of a chemical reaction. Oxidizers themselves are not combustible, but they support combustion when combined with a fuel. While oxygen is the most common oxidizer, there are other substances that fall into the category. **Table 3.3** lists other common oxidizers.

Table 3.3
Common Oxidizers
Bromates
Bromine
Chlorates
Chlorine
Fluorine
Iodine
Nitrates
Nitric acid
Nitrites
Perchlorates
Permanganates
Peroxides

Source: NFPA 49, Hazardous Chemicals Data

For the purposes of this discussion, the oxygen in the air around us is considered the primary oxidizing agent. Normally air consists of about 21 percent oxygen. At room temperature (70°F or 21°C), combustion is supported at oxygen concentrations as low as 14 percent. Research shows, however, that as temperatures in a compartment fire (a room or other confined space) increase, lower concentrations of oxygen are needed to support flaming combustion (fire). In studies of compartment fires, flaming combustion has been observed at post-flashover temperature conditions (known as the fully developed and decay stages) when oxygen concentrations have been very low (2% or less.)

NOTE: For additional information, see the Fire Development section of this chapter.

When oxygen concentrations exceed 21 percent, the atmosphere is said to be oxygen enriched. Under these conditions, materials exhibit very different burning characteristics. Materials that

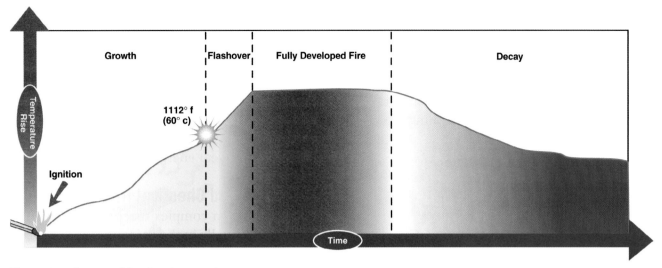

Figure 3.15 Stages of fire development in a compartment.

compartment fire is defined as a fire that occurs within such a space. The growth and development of a compartment fire is usually controlled by the availability of fuel and oxygen. When the amount of fuel available to burn is limited, the fire is said to be fuel controlled. When the amount of available oxygen is limited, the condition is called ventilation controlled.

Recently, researchers have attempted to describe compartment fires in terms of stages or phases that occur as the fire develops. These stages are as follows:

- Ignition
- Growth
- Flashover
- Fully developed
- Decay

The development of a compartment fire in terms of time and temperature is shown in **Figure 3.15**. It should be noted that the stages are an attempt to describe the complex reaction that is occurring as a fire develops in a space with no suppression action taken. The ignition and development of a compartment fire are very complex and influenced by many variables. As a result, all fires may not develop through each of the stages described. The information is presented to depict fire as a dynamic event that is dependent on many factors for its growth and development.

Ignition

Ignition describes the period when the four elements of the fire tetrahedron come together and combustion begins. The physical act of ignition can be piloted (caused by an arc, spark, or flame) or nonpiloted (caused when a material reaches its autoignition temperature as the result of heating without a pilot source), such as spontaneous ignition. At this point, the fire is small and generally confined to the material (fuel) first ignited. All fires — in an open area or within a compartment — occur as a result of some type of ignition.

Growth

Shortly after ignition, a fire plume begins to form above the burning fuel. As the plume develops, it begins to draw or entrain air from the surrounding space into the column. The initial growth is similar to that of an unconfined fire, with the growth a function of the fuel first ignited. Unlike an unconfined fire, the plume in a compartment is rapidly affected by its boundaries, namely the ceiling and walls. The first impact is the amount of air that is entrained into the plume. Because the air is cooler than the hot gases generated by the fire, the air has a cooling effect on the plume temperatures. The location of the fuel package in relation to the compartment walls determines the amount of air that is entrained and thus the amount of cooling that takes place. The location also affects the development of the plume by restricting the volume it occupies as well as the amount of radiation feedback from wall surfaces. Given the same fuel package, those that are located near walls will have higher plume temperatures and taller plumes. This is because less air is entrained and the fire plume is restricted by the wall, which results in greater radiation feedback. Fuel packages located in corners will have the highest plume temperatures and the tallest plumes (**Figure 3.16, p. 54**). This factor significantly impacts the rate that the temperatures are increased in the hot gas layer above the fire. As the hot gases rise, they begin to spread outward when they hit the ceiling. This spread continues until the walls that make up the compartment are reached. The depth of the gas layer then begins to increase.

The temperatures in the compartment during this period are dependent on the amount of heat that is lost through conduction into the compartment ceiling and walls as the gases flow over them, the location of the initial fuel package, the resulting air entrainment, and the depth of the upper hot gas layer. Research shows that the plume gas temperatures decrease as the distance from the center line of the plume increases. **Figures 3.17 a and b, p. 54,** show the plume in a typical compartment fire and the factors that impact the temperature of the developing hot gas layer.

The growth stage continues if enough fuel and oxygen are available. Compartment fires in the growth stage are generally fuel controlled. As the fire grows, the overall temperature in the compartment increases, as does the temperature of the gas layer at the ceiling level (**Figures 3.18 a and b, p. 55**).

Flameover/Rollover

The terms *flameover* and *rollover* are used to describe a condition where flames move through or across the unburned gases at ceiling level during a fire's progression and prior to flashover. Flameover is distinguished from flashover by its involvement of only the fire gases and not the surfaces of other fuel packages within a compartment. This condition may occur during the growth stage as the hot gas layer forms at the ceiling of the compartment. Flames may be observed in the layer when the combustible gases reach their ignition temperature

and there is sufficient oxygen present. While the flames add to the total heat generated in the compartment and may lead to flashover, this condition is not flashover. A flameover will not always result in the ignition of target fuels within a compartment but may result in fire patterns on walls and other combustible building elements with which the gases are in direct contact (**Figures 3.19 a and b, p. 56**).

Flashover

Flashover is the transition between the growth and the fully developed fire stages and is not a specific event such as ignition. During flashover, conditions in the compartment change very rapidly as the fire changes from one that is dominated by the burning of the materials first ignited to one that involves all of the combustibles within the compartment. The hot gas layer that develops at the ceiling level during the growth stage causes radiant heating of combustible materials remote from the origin of the fire (**Figure 3.20, p. 56**). Typically, radiant energy (heat flux, or the rate of heat transfer across a surface) from the hot gas layer exceeds 20 kW/m^2 at the floor when flashover occurs. This radiant heating causes pyrolysis to take place in the combustible materials in the compartment. The gases generated during this time are heated to their ignition temperatures by the radiant energy from the gas layer at the ceiling (**Figures 3.21 a and b, p. 57**).

While flashover is indicated in many ways by scientists, most base their determination of the onset of flashover on the average temperature in the heated upper layer (600°C or 1,112°F) and the 20 kW per square meter heat flux that results in the nearly simultaneous ignition of all of the combustible contents in the space.

Just prior to flashover, several things are happening within the burning compartment. The temperatures are rapidly increasing, additional fuel packages are becoming involved, and the fuel packages in the compartment are nearing their autoignition temperatures. As flashover occurs, the combustible materials in the compartment and the pyrolysis gases ignite. The result is full-room involvement. The heat release from a fully developed room at flashover can be on the order of 10,000 kW or more.

Figure 3.16 When the developing fire plume is restricted by a wall, greater radiation feedback occurs in the compartment. *Courtesy of CT Office of State Fire Marshal.*

Figures 3.17 a and b Initially, the temperature of the fire gases decreases as they move away from the centerline of the plume. *B courtesy of CT Office of State Fire Marshal.*

DEVELOPMENT OF CEILING LAYER

Figures 3.18 a and b As the fire grows, the overall temperature in the compartment increases as does the temperature of the gas layer at the ceiling level. *B courtesy of CT Office of State Fire Marshal.*

Figures 3.19 a and b Examples of rollover. Note the beginning of flame progression across the ceiling in the photograph. *B courtesy of CT Office of State Fire Marshal.*

Figure 3.20 The radiant heat (red arrows) from the hot-gas layer at the ceiling heats combustible materials, which produces vapors (green arrows).

• Room temperature in excess of 900°F (483°C)
• All combustible surfaces are burning as are the gases

Recirculating Smoke

FLASHOVER

Figures 3.21 a and b When flashover occurs, all combustibles in the compartment ignite simultaneously. *B courtesy of CT Office of State Fire Marshal.*

Occupants who have not escaped from a compartment before flashover occurs are not likely to survive. Firefighters who find themselves in a compartment at flashover are at extreme risk even while wearing their personal protective equipment.

Fully Developed

The fully developed fire stage occurs when all combustible materials in the compartment are involved in fire. During this period of time, the burning fuels in the compartment are releasing the maximum amount of heat possible for the available fuel packages and producing large volumes of fire gases. The heat released and the volume of fire gases produced depends on the number and size of the ventilation openings in the compartment. The fire frequently becomes ventilation controlled; therefore, large volumes of unburned gases are produced. During this stage, hot unburned fire gases are flowing from the compartment of origin into adjacent spaces or compartments. These gases ignite as they enter a space where air is more abundant (**Figures 3.22 a and b**).

Decay

As the available fuel in the compartment is consumed by the fire, the rate of heat release begins to decline. Once again the fire becomes fuel con-

Figures 3.22 a and b When the fire is fully developed, the burning fuels in the compartment are releasing the maximum amount of heat possible. *B courtesy of CT Office of State Fire Marshal.*

trolled, the amount of fire diminishes, and the temperatures within the compartment begin to decline. The remaining mass of glowing embers can, however, result in moderately high temperatures in the compartment for some time.

Factors That Impact Fire Development

As the compartment fire progresses from ignition to decay in the previous illustration, several factors impact the behavior of a fire and its development within a compartment:

- Size, number, and arrangement of ventilation openings
- Volume of the compartment
- Thermal properties of the compartment enclosures
- Ceiling height of the compartment
- Size, composition, and location of the fuel package that is first ignited
- Availability and locations of additional fuel packages (target fuels)

For a fire to develop, there must be sufficient air available to support burning beyond the ignition stage. The size and number of ventilation openings in a compartment determine how the fire develops within the space. The compartment size and shape and the ceiling height determine whether or not a significant hot gas layer will form. The location of the initial fuel package is also very important in the development of the hot gas layer. The plumes of burning fuel packages in the center of a compartment entrain more air and are cooler than those against walls or in corners of the compartment.

The temperatures that develop in a burning compartment are the direct result of the energy released as the fuels burn. Because matter and energy are conserved, any loss in mass caused by the fire is converted to energy. In a fire, the resulting energy is mainly in the form of heat, and to a lesser degree, light. The amount of heat energy released over time in a fire is called the heat release rate (HRR). HRR is measured in Btus per second or kilowatts (kW). The heat release rate is directly related to the amount of fuel being consumed over time and the heat of combustion (the amount of heat a specific

mass of the substance can give off when burned) of the fuel being burned. See **Table 3.6** for maximum heat release rates for several common items. This information is presented to give representative numbers for typical fuel items.

Table 3.6 Representative Peak Heat Release Rates (Unconfirmed Burning)			
Fuel	(kg)	(lb)	Peak HRR (kW)
Wastebasket, small	0.7 – 6.1	1.5 – 3	4-18
Trash bags, 11 gal with Mixed plastic and paper trash	1.1 – 3.4	2½ – 7½	140-350
Cotton mattress	11.8 – 13.2	26 – 29	40-970
TV sets	31.3 – 32.7	69 – 72	120 – 290
Plastic trash bags/ paper trash	1.2 – 14.1	2.6 – 31	120-350
PVC waiting room chair, metal frame	15.4	34	270
Cotton easy chair	17.7 – 31.8	39 – 70	290-370
Gasoline/kerosene in 0.61 m2 (2 ft.2) pool	19	--	400
Christmas trees, dry	6.4 – 7.3	14 – 16	500-650
Polyurethane mattress	3.2 – 14.1	7 – 31	810 – 2630
Polyurethane easy chair	12.2 – 27.7	27 – 61	1350 – 1990
Polyurethane sofa	51.3	113	3120

Reprinted with permission from NFPA 921-2004, *Guide for Fire and Explosion Investigations*, Copyright © 2004, National Fire Protection Association, Quincy, MA 02169. This reprinted material is not the complete and official position of the NFPA on the referenced subject, which is represented only by the standard in its entirety.

Emergency response personnel should be able to recognize the damage from fuel packages in a building or compartment and use this information as part of the analysis of the fire scene. Materials with high heat release rates, such as polyurethane foam, padded furniture, mattresses, stacks of wooden pallets, and ignitable liquids, would be expected to burn rapidly once ignition occurs. Fires in materials with lower heat release rates would be expected to take longer to develop. In general, low-density materials (such as polyurethane foam) burn faster and have a higher HRR than do higher density materials (cotton padding) of similar makeup.

One final relationship between the heat generated in a fire and fuel packages is the ignition of fuel packages that are remote from the first package ignited. The heat generated in a compartment fire is transmitted from the initial fuel package to other fuels in the space by convection and radiation. The heat rising in the initial fire plume is transported by convection. Radiation plays an increasingly significant role in the transition from a growing fire to a fully developed fire in a room. As the hot gas layer forms at the ceiling, it radiates energy to the other fuel packages in the compartment. These remote fuel packages are sometimes called target fuels. As the radiant energy transfer (flux) increases, the target fuels begin to reach their ignition temperatures.

Special Considerations

Several conditions or situations occur during the course of a fire's development that should be discussed. These conditions can occur as a fire proceeds through the stages of growth and development. This section provides an overview of these conditions and the potential damage that may result during the fire.

Backdraft

As the fire grows in a compartment, large volumes of hot unburned fire gases can collect in unventilated spaces. These gases may be at or above their ignition temperatures but have insufficient oxygen available for actual ignition to take place. Any action that allows air to mix with these hot gases can result in an explosive ignition called a backdraft.

Should a backdraft occur, the ERP will observe overpressure damage in the building. Homes have been moved from their foundations and walls of multiple-story buildings have been blown off as a result of a backdraft.

WARNING!

Many firefighters have been killed or injured as a result of backdraft. The potential for backdraft can be reduced with proper vertical ventilation (opening at highest point). Because the unburned gases rise, the building or space should be opened at the highest possible point to allow them to escape before entry is made (Figure 3.23, p. 61).

The following conditions during the fire fighting operations may indicate the potential for a backdraft to occur:

• Pressurized smoke exiting small openings
• Black smoke becoming dense gray-yellow
• Confinement and excessive heat
• Little or no visible flame
• Smoke leaving the building in puffs or at intervals (appearance of breathing)
• Smoke-stained windows

Products of Combustion

As a fuel burns, the composition of the material is chemically changed. This change results in the production of new substances and in the generation of energy **(Figure 3.24, p. 61)**. As a fuel is burned, some of it is actually consumed. The Law of Conservation of Mass tells us that any mass that is lost converts to energy. In the case of fire, this energy is in the form of light and heat. Burning also results in the generation of airborne fire gases, particles, and liquids (aerosols). An aerosol can be defined as a suspension of liquid or solid particles in air or gas. These materials have been referred to throughout this chapter as products of combustion or smoke. The heat generated during a fire is one of the products of combustion. In addition to being responsible for the spread of a fire, heat also causes

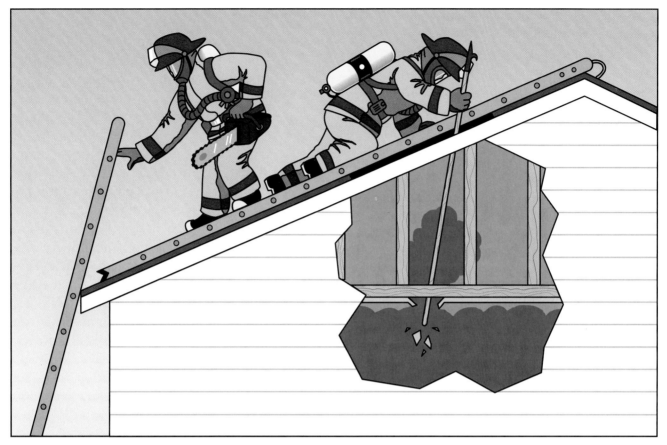

Figure 3.23 Releasing heat, smoke, and other products of combustion through the roof will reduce the possibility of backdraft and aid in interior fire fighting.

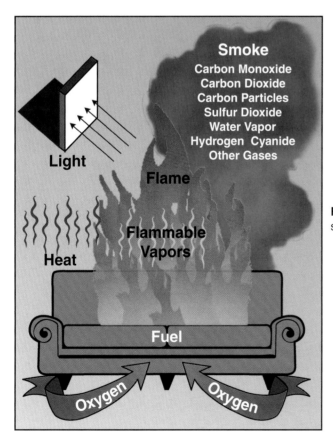

Figure 3.24 The four products of combustion are heat, light, smoke, and fire gases.

burns, dehydration, heat exhaustion, and injury to a person's respiratory tract.

While the heat energy from a fire is a danger to anyone directly exposed to it, smoke is the cause of most deaths in fires. The materials that make up smoke vary from fuel to fuel, but generally all smoke can be considered toxic and may be lethal.

The most common of the hazardous substances contained in smoke is carbon monoxide (CO). While CO is not the most dangerous of the materials found in smoke, it is almost always present when combustion occurs. While someone may be killed or injured by breathing a variety of toxic substances in smoke, carbon monoxide is the one that is most easily detected in the blood of fire victims and thus most often reported. Because the substances contained in smoke developed in compartment fires (either alone or in combination) are deadly, firefighters and any fire investigators must use SCBA for protection when operating in smoke. Toxic products of combustion are still present at fire scenes after extinguishment, so ERPs and fire investigators need to monitor the atmosphere and wear breathing protection as needed.

Summary

In the process of determining the origin and cause of a fire, the ERP will use his or her knowledge of fire behavior to establish theories regarding the fire cause and then to test those theories for validity. Everyone associated with the origin and cause investigation will attempt to determine the initial fuel package that was ignited, the source of ignition (source of energy), and how the two came together to cause ignition. The ERP will have to examine the fire scene in order to establish the area of origin. In doing this, he or she will have to evaluate how the fire developed after ignition until it was extinguished. To accomplish this task, the ERP will use knowledge of the elements of the fire tetrahedron and the phases of the combustion process. They will also attempt to determine if their theories regarding ignition, the fuels first ignited, and the spread of the fire to subsequent fuel packages are probable, and then use the information to explain their findings. How this information is used to make origin and cause determination is the subject of the remainder of this manual.

Chapter 4:
Determining the Area of Fire Origin

Figure 4.17 Photograph the fuel cap, if present, and note if the gas tank seems to have been tampered with. *Courtesy of Donny Howard, Yates & Associates.*

Examining the Electrical System

Fires caused by the vehicle electrical system must occur within a circuit that is energized at the time of the fire. Only a limited number of energized circuits are present after the ignition has been turned off. The ERP may need the assistance of an expert familiar with the electrical system of the model of vehicle involved. Hybrid cars (electric/gasoline powered vehicles) present a unique ignition scenario and danger because the battery powering the electric motor carries as much as 500 volts, more than 40 times the strength of a standard battery.

Other Vehicles

The causes of fires in other vehicles do not differ significantly from automobile fires. The only differences between automobile fires and those in other vehicles are the quantity of fuel and other ignitable liquids and gases, the presence of additional competent ignition sources, the composition of the involved vehicle, and any materials being transported (**Figures 4.18 a and b**). Some examples of these vehicles are:

- Over-the-road trucks (tractor-trailers)
- Construction equipment
- Agricultural equipment
- Motor homes and other recreational vehicles
- Fifth wheels
- Watercraft
- Motorcycles
- Aircraft

NOTE: For further information on vehicle fires, see NFPA 921, 2004 edition, Chapter 25, Motor Vehicle Fires, and the IFSTA **Principles of Vehicle Extrication** manual.

> The ERP should be cautioned about the evidentiary value of any vehicle. As with an appliance, do not loosen, move or remove parts, components, or switches.

Figures 4.18 a and b Investigating fire cause in other vehicles is handled much the same way as automobiles. Be sure to note materials transported, type of fuel used, and alternate ignition sources. *A courtesy of Donny Howard, Yates & Associates. B courtesy of Chris E. Mickal.*

Wildfires

Emergency response personnel must be aware that wildfire origin and cause determination is a highly specialized field of study, one that is far different in scope and process from structural fires. When confronted with this type of fire, it is often prudent to contact a qualified fire investigator and preserve the scene while awaiting for his or her arrival **(Figure 4.19)**.

NOTE: Further information regarding wildfire investigations can be found in the following publications:

- The IFSTA **Wildland Fire Fighting for Structural Firefighters** manual
- NFPA 921, 2004 ed., Chapter 26, Wildfire Investigation
- *Wildfire Cause Determination Handbook, available from National Interagency Fire Center,* 3833 S. Development Avenue, Boise, Idaho 83705-5354

Web site: http://www.nifc.gov/news/nicc.html

Summary

Determining the origin of a fire may be a complex task. Witnesses must be interviewed and evidence from the fire scene must be identified, properly collected, documented and preserved. Only carefully studied evidence will help the fire investigator accurately determine the cause of a fire, and only carefully preserved and documented evidence will be useful during any legal proceedings. It is the culmination of all the facts that will lead to an accurate determination of the area of origin and the fire cause. Outside experts may be consulted to assist the ERP in interpreting potential evidence. Finally, if ERPs are unable to make a determination of the area of origin, a qualified fire investigator should be called for assistance as soon as possible while the ERP secures the scene to preserve potential evidence.

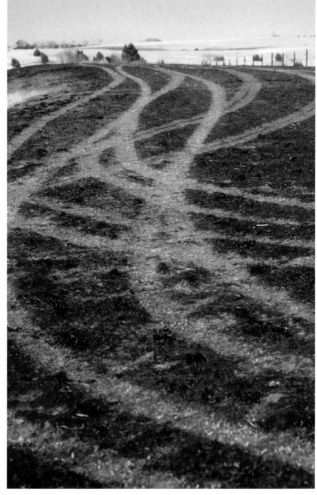

Figure 4.19 While waiting for the arrival of a fire investigator, see that vehicles are not driven through burned areas, thus destroying evidence.

Chapter 5:
Determining and Classifying the Cause of Fires and Explosions

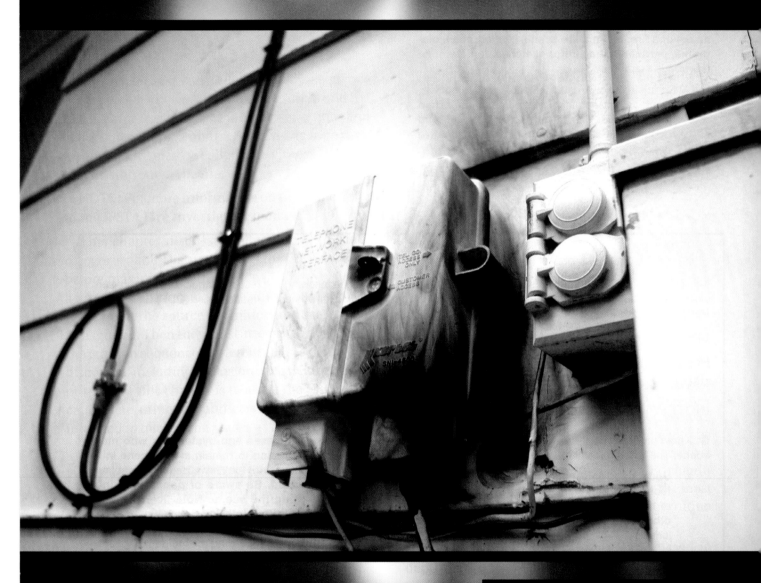

Courtesy of Donny Howard, Yates & Associates.

Figure 5.1 The source of ignition is likely to be chemical, mechanical, or electrical. *A courtesy of Michael Wieder.*

for light combustible materials. The smoking materials must transmit sufficient energy to the combustible prior to self-extinguishment and the combustible typically must be insulated to result in sufficient temperature for ignition.

As an example, a lit cigarette left on a wooden table will not generate enough heat to cause combustion; however, that same cigarette dropped between a couch cushion or a pillow can cause enough heat for combustion due to its being insulated.

Open Flames

- **Matches.** Matches in a flaming state provide an available heat source for common combustibles.

- **Candles.** Candles produce sufficient heat energy to cause ignition of ordinary combustible materials **(Figure 5.2)**. Methods of heat transfer can be where the fuel is in contact with the candle (conduction), where the heat comes into contact with combustibles above the flame (convection), or if the fuel is in very close proximity to the flame (radiation).

Figure 5.2 Decorative candles have become very popular in recent years. If they are unattended or disturbed by pets, however, they are an excellent source of ignition. *Courtesy of Mary Stone.*

Arcs and Sparks

- **Arcs.** An arc can be defined as a luminous discharge of electricity across a gap. An arc develops sufficient energy (above 2,000°F [1 093°C]) to ignite many light combustible materials, as well as flammable gas and vapors **(Figure 5.3, p. 81)**.

Figure 5.3 The arcs caused by power tools are always hazardous if they contact an ignition source.

- **Sparks.** A spark is a moving particle of solid material that radiates energy for a brief period of time. It is a competent ignition source for a flammable gas or vapor.

- **Electrostatic discharge (ESD).** Static electricity can be defined as an accumulation of electrical charges on opposing surfaces created by the separation of unlike materials or by the movement of surfaces. The movement of this charge from positive to negative results in an arc, which releases enough energy to ignite combustible gases, vapors, or dust.

- **Friction.** The heat of friction is created by two surfaces moving against each other. This movement generates heat and/or sparks, which may be sufficient to ignite adjacent combustible materials. For example, friction-produced heat

can be generated by a truck tire rubbing against a wheel well on a vehicle, or by a poorly lubricated shaft bearing.

Hot Surfaces and Objects

A hot surface or object typically provides energy through conduction to the first material ignited and must have sufficient energy to ignite combustibles. For example, a dish towel left on top of a range heating element is sufficient to start combustion; a car that catches fire on dry grass can ignite surrounding brush **(Figure 5.4)**.

Figure 5.4. The heat from this burning car ignited nearby grass through conduction.

Natural Sources

Sunlight itself does not provide sufficient energy to be classified as an ignition source. When refracted, however, sunlight's energy can be concentrated sufficiently to ignite nearby combustibles. This is evident when light travels through a magnifying glass (convex surface), creating a pinpoint of light to be concentrated on the surface of a piece of paper **(Figures 5.5 a and b, p. 82)**. Another source of natural energy is lightning. A lightning discharge is not a single bolt, but several strikes within a minute amount of time. The force can be destructive, sometimes generating over 100,000 volts and

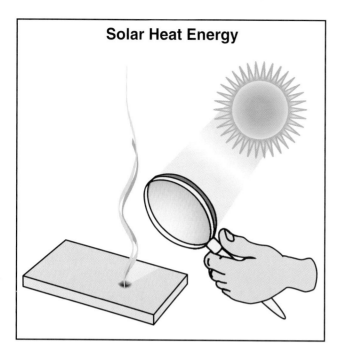

Solar Heat Energy

Figures 5.5 a and b Concentrated sunlight is an effective ignition source. Lightning is a well-known source of ignition. *B courtesy of Tony Bacon.*

providing sufficient energy to ignite ordinary combustibles.

Self-Heating (spontaneous heating)

Some materials are capable of generating heat through chemical or biological actions. If this resulting heat is not dissipated more quickly than it is generated, ignition of common combustibles may occur. An example is a saturated oil, such as boiled linseed oil, in contact with cloth or freshly baled moist hay.

NOTE: **Table 3.5** on p. 50 of this manual lists materials subject to spontaneous heating.

Material First Ignited

A key component in making a fire cause determination is identifying, if possible, the material first ignited. NFPA 921 says, "The first material ignited (initial fuel) is that which first sustains combustion beyond the igniting source." For example, consider a house fire resulting from a burning candle on a windowsill. The burning candle would not be the first material ignited; the curtains that were ignited by the open candle flame would be the first material ignited.

Physical Properties of Fuels

When the ERP is trying to identify the first fuel ignited, a number of factors should be considered. One factor is surface-to-mass ratio. To further understand this concept, consider how difficult it is to ignite a 2 x 4 with a match and how easy it is to ignite shavings from the same block of wood. Although both materials are the same, their ignitability is very different. Another factor is orientation of the fuel, namely vertical versus horizontal position. For example, a heat source applied to the end of a 1 x 6-inch board held in the vertical position is more likely to ignite the board than the same heat source applied to the middle of that board held in a horizontal position.

NOTE: Refer to Chapter 3 for discussion and illustration of surface-to-mass ratio and orientation of ignitable materials.

Form and Type of Material First Ignited

The form in which a fuel exists just prior to the incident is relevant to the fire investigation. Fuels can exist in solid, liquid, vapor, or gas form. As a general rule, solids are most difficult to ignite and gases are the easiest. Generally, a solid fuel must be turned into a vapor before ignition will occur. When the ERP is examining potential first material ignited, consideration must be given to the state of the fuel package prior to the ignition. Wood, for example, must be heated to the point where the surface is starting to off-gas before it will ignite. Likewise, it is the vapor on the surface of a liquid mass that will ignite. Depending on the type of liquid, it may or may not require heating before sufficient vapors form to permit ignition. Gases, because of their state, are in a more readily ignitable form.

Ignition Sequence

The ignition sequence is the sequence of events that allows a competent ignition source to ignite a fuel package. Consider the candle and curtain example used above. A candle sitting some distance from the curtains, with the window closed so that neither the candle flame nor the curtains are moving, will not result in an ignition sequence. However, if the window is open and the curtains move close to the flame, the ignition sequence is completed when the curtains move over the flame and ignite **(Figure 5.6)**. Therefore, the ERP will have to determine if the window was open or closed at the time the fire ignited before the ignition sequence can be analyzed.

To determine the ignition sequence, the ERP should develop a series of hypotheses and test each one by asking questions and gathering more information if necessary. In testing the hypothesis regarding the ignition sequence by using the candle example, some questions that need to be addressed are as follows:

1. Was the candle lit? (a competent ignition source)

2. Of what material were the curtains made? Was the material capable of igniting and sustaining a flame ? (first material ignited)

3. Was the window open or closed? (part of the ignition sequence)

4. What was the distance from the candle to the curtains? (part of the ignition sequence)

Figure 5.6 An open window and a breeze that allows an ignitable material to contact a heat source is a simple ignition sequence.

5. Was there a wind or breeze that day? (part of the ignition sequence)

These are examples of the type of questions that one should pose when testing theories of a possible ignition sequence.

NOTE: Refer to Chapter 4 for an illustration of the Scientific Method of problem solving.

When evaluating ignition sequences, the ERP may need to consider whether someone's action or omission (failure to act) was one of the events that brought together the competent ignition source with the first material ignited. An example of an action pertaining to an ignition sequence would be dropping a lit match onto a gasoline spill. An example of an omission would be neglecting to replace a frayed extension cord underneath a carpet **(Figure 5.7)**.

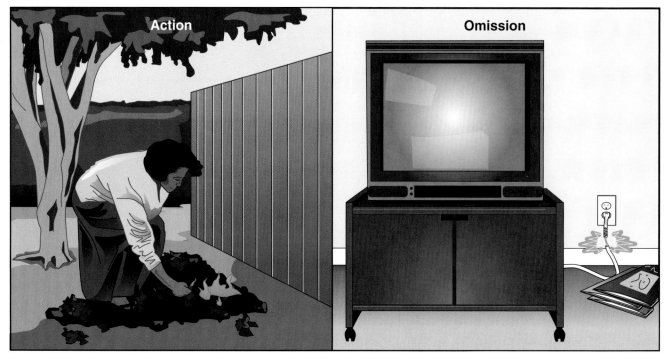

Figure 5.7 Did the ignition sequence result from action or failure to act? Did the people involved intend to cause harm or was it an accident?

Another important factor to consider is whether there is evidence that the action or omission was done with intent to cause the fire. An ERP may have to consider intent when categorizing or classifying a fire as either accidental or incendiary. Using one of the above examples, a person may have intended to light a match for a cigarette and then discarded the match, not realizing that gasoline was present or that the dark spot on the pavement was gasoline. In this circumstance the fire would be classified as accidental. The same action, however, would be classified as incendiary if the person knew that gasoline was present and threw the lit match onto the gasoline spill, knowing that a fire would be likely to start. Another example would be placing a pan of cooking oil on an energized cook stove or range that resulted in the intentional ignition of the oil; such action would be classified as incendiary. If this same fire occurred through the inattention of the user, however, the fire would be classified as accidental.

Ignition Scenarios

Depending of the source of the heat, the ERP may find evidence that is recognizable, such as an electrical space heater with combustible materials stacked against it **(Figure 5.8)**. In other cases, the actual heat source may not remain at the point of origin, but it may have been altered or completely destroyed by the fire. The ignition source must have the ability to ignite the first material and is therefore classified as a competent ignition source. As an example, an electrical arc is a competent ignition source for paper but not a competent ignition source for a 2 x 4 board. The physical state of the first fuel ignited has a significant impact on the amount of energy required for its ignition.

Electricity

Electrical equipment is a potential source of heat energy **(Figure 5.9)**. The fire scene examination involves evaluating these potential heat sources and determining if they can be eliminated or identified as the source of ignition. A common example of an electrical ignition source is a short circuit. The arcing or sparking resulting from the short circuit may provide temperature for ignition of light combustibles. More likely, resistance heating may provide sufficient temperature if the resulting heat is not allowed to dissipate.

Appliances

An appliance, whether electrical or fuel gas, may provide a competent ignition source, even under scenarios in which it has not failed. For example, a water heater is a potential ignition source for

Figure 5.8 The heat source may be readily identifiable, such as combustibles left too close to a heater.

a cardboard box placed next to its combustion chamber. Likewise, a failed electrical or gas appliance may provide a competent source of ignition through an electrical high-limit switch or a malfunctioning gas regulator.

If an appliance is suspected to be the cause of a fire, **DO NOT DISASSEMBLE THE APPLIANCE OR MOVE OR MANIPULATE ANY OF THE CONTROLS.**

Incendiary Devices

An incendiary device is designed and used to start a fire. Incendiary devices may leave evidence of their existence, especially the metal parts of mechanical or electrical devices (**Figure 5.10, p. 86**). An incendiary device may be a common appliance that has been altered to fail and start a fire, or has been used as a timing device to allow a delayed ignition. An incendiary device does not have to be complex. It can be as simple as a cigarette and a matchbook. More than one device may be used, and sometimes a faulty device can be found.

WARNING!

If a suspected or incendiary device that has failed to function is found, immediately call a trained explosive technician.

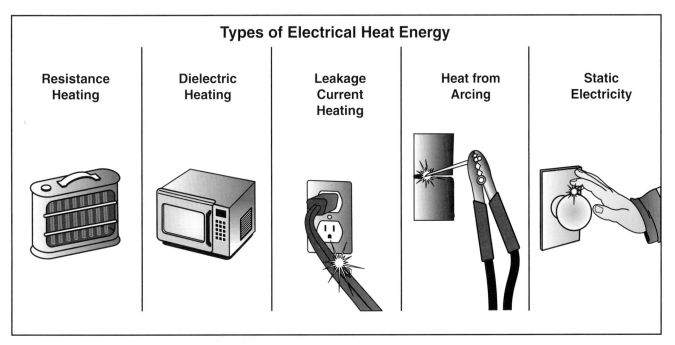

Figure 5.9 Nearly every home and business has many potential sources of electrical heat energy.

Figure 5.10 The metal parts of electrical or mechanical incendiary devices, such as this timer, may be found in the debris of the fire.

Explosions

Assistance in investigating a bombing can be obtained by calling local or state law enforcement agencies. They can then notify the Bureau of Alcohol, Tobacco, and Firearms (ATF), Federal Bureau of Investigations (FBI), or a military installation for assistance. In Canada, notify the police authority having jurisdiction. It is not uncommon for there to be a second device that may pose a hazard to responding personnel. If your agency is not trained in bombing/explosives investigations, immediately contact specialists.

Establish a perimeter a minimum of one and one-half times (150 percent) the distance from the apparent seat of the explosion to the furthermost location of discovered fragments. This perimeter may later have to be expanded as the search proceeds (**Figure 5.11**).

Explosions caused by high explosives, such as dynamite, and those caused by low explosives, such as black or smokeless powder, have different characteristics. These differences are the result of the reaction time. Low explosives deflagrate but generally do not detonate. A detonation takes place at or above the speed of sound (1,129 fps) [342 mps] while deflagration is below the speed of sound. All explosions produce high quantities of heat; however, temperatures differ between detonations and deflagrations. Extremely high temperatures of short duration are characteristic of a detonation while deflagrations produce lower temperatures over a greater time. High and low explosives pro-

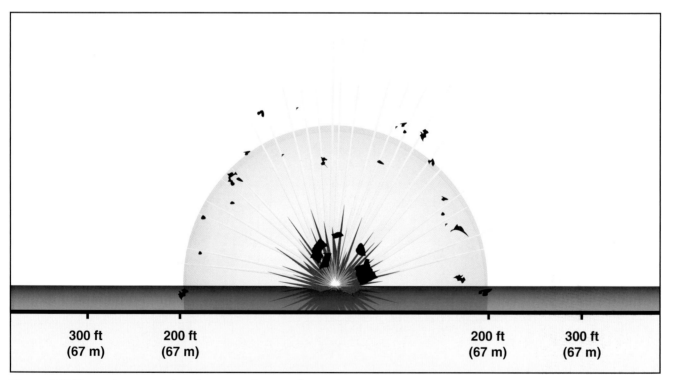

| 300 ft (67 m) | 200 ft (67 m) | | 200 ft (67 m) | 300 ft (67 m) |

Figure 5.11 The perimeter needs to be one and one-half times (150 percent) the distance from the apparent seat of the explosion to the furthermost location of discovered fragments.

Figure 5.12 High explosives have a shattering effect.

duce different effects. This difference is important because it often provides the first clue as to which type likely caused the explosion.

High Explosives

High explosives have a very rapid rate of decomposition, and the force exerted by their detonation produces a shattering effect (**Figure 5.12**). The shattering effect decreases sharply with increasing distance from the seat of the explosion, and damage radiates from the point of origin in all directions. Dynamite exploded on a concrete or earthen floor would expend some of its energy downward, leaving a depression.

Low Explosives

Deflagrations can usually be identified by their overall destructiveness without excessive fragmentation. Low explosives have a tendency to lift, heave, and push. The building will have a characteristic "pushed out" appearance (**Figure 5.13**).

Because low-explosive deflagrations do not tend to shatter objects, window frames in walls still standing may be pushed out with the glass still intact. Lights, such as fluorescent tubes, would not necessarily be broken.

Figure 5.13 Low explosives give a structure a pushed-out appearance.

Figure 5.14 Pressurized containers may fail in a dramatic way.

Flammable Gases

Flammable gases may also ignite and burn with explosive force when confined. In some cases their containers may rupture with considerable energy release and fragmentation, followed by a rapid burning of the vaporized product (**Figure 5.14**).

Through careful examination, the type of gas involved in an explosion may be determined. A heavier-than-air gas, such as propane, seeks lower areas and generally concentrates in the basement or at floor level. A lighter-than-air gas, such as natural gas, generally rises to the roof or ceiling. The blast damage from an explosion may occur where the optimum mixture of gas was located or may occur at the weakest point of the container or structure. The pressure developed at the time of the explosion in seeking the path of least resistance may blow out portions of walls because they were less securely anchored. The optimum mixture is a concentration level usually midpoint between the lower explosive limit (LEL) and upper explosive limit (UEL).

There have been a number of cases in which people have been killed or injured in dwellings that had no gas service. Escaping gas can enter a building in many ways. It may travel through or along the outside of service pipes, such as water pipes, drains, and electrical or telephone conduits, or it may come up into a basement through untrapped drains or sewers. Escaping gas may travel through the soil and enter the building through a porous block or cracked concrete wall. Gas may travel a long distance underground, particularly if it is prevented from escaping to the air because of frozen topsoil,

pavement, or concrete. The mercaptan added to gas to give it its distinctive odor is sometimes leached from the gas during travel through soil through a process known as adsorption. When this process happens, there will be no warning smell of gas accumulation.

The ERP should also be aware that even in areas not serviced by fuel gas, a naturally occurring accumulation of methane may be present.

Dust

A deflagration resulting from dust may resemble a gas explosion and is usually very destructive. A grain handling facility is a good example of an area with a high risk of dust explosion. The finer the dust particles, the more violent the resulting explosion. Dust explosions may start with a relatively minor explosion and then develop into a series of explosions of considerable magnitude -- a chain reaction caused by the first explosion releasing other dust on shelves, rafters, and the like. A dust explosion depends on several factors, including size of particles, dust concentration, amount of oxygen, as well as an ignition source.

Wildfire Causes and Indicators

IFSTA defines wildfire, occasionally called a wildland or vegetation fire as "unplanned, unwanted, and uncontrolled fire in vegetative fuels such as grass, brush, or timberland involving uncultivated lands requiring suppression action. These fires can threaten structures or other improvements." Some of the more common wildfire causes are discussed in this section. Each cause has certain telltale characteristics that ERPs should look for:

- **Lightning.** Trees, poles, and logs struck by lightning may show strike marks on their surfaces. Live trees and deadwood with a high moisture content may literally explode when the heat from a lightning bolt instantly turns the internal moisture to steam. The explosion often splinters trees, logs, and roots (**Figure 5.15**). Soil at the site of a strike may be disturbed, and there may be fused, glassy clumps beneath the surface.

- **Campfires.** Even a campsite that burns completely leaves evidence of its existence (**Figure 5.16**). Metal or glass containers and the metal grommets from a tent may be found. The campfire itself may be detected by a circle of rocks enclosing a large concentration of ash, or there may be ash from pieces of wood lying in a definite pattern.

- **Smoking materials.** While it is extremely difficult to start a wildfire with a cigarette, under ideal conditions it can happen. Fires resulting from discarded smoking materials (matches, lighters, or cigarette or cigar butts) most often occur in grass and other extremely fine fuels when the relative humidity is less than 25 percent (**Figure 5.17**).

- **Debris burning.** Fires at dump sites or other debris-burning operations may spread to surrounding wildland areas. A burn barrel or incinerator in or near the burned area, a history of other fires at this location, or windy conditions at the time the fire started, may indicate that the debris-burning operation was the cause of the fire. Ideally, one or more witnesses will confirm that a debris-burning operation was the cause.

- **Incendiary fires.** Some of the common indicators of incendiary fires are two or more fires set (often along roads or trails) or fires set in places frequently used for parties or gatherings. Igniting devices, such as fusees or matchbooks, may be found at the point of origin. Delayed igniting devices are sometimes found (**Figure 5.18, p. 90**). These devices may consist of combinations of items not normally found in a wildland — cigarettes, matches, candles, rope, wire, tape, or rubber bands.

- **Heavy equipment use.** Heavy equipment operations may start wildfires in a number of ways. Operating heavy equipment without a spark arrestor (or with a defective spark arrestor) on the exhaust pipe is a frequent cause of wildfires (**Figure 5.19, p.90**). When the equipment's steel blade or tracks strike rocks, a spark can be produced that is capable of igniting very fine, dry fuels.

- **Railroads.** Railroads are sometimes sources of wildfires. These fires may result from railroad crews intentionally burning rights-of-way or old railroad ties, hot fragments from brake shoes, fusees, flares, or crews discarding lighted smoking materials along the rights-of-way (**Figure 5.20, p. 90**).

Figure 5.15 Lightning caused the splits in this tree. *Courtesy of NIFC.*

Figure 5.16 The flags in this photo mark the trail where the campfire spread to the surrounding combustible materials.

Figure 5.17 The remains of the match that started this fire were found at the point of origin of the fire. *Courtesy of Hugh Graham.*

Figure 5.18 A typical cigarette-match combination timing device. *Courtesy of Bill Lellis.*

Summary

Many factors should be considered when determining the cause of a fire. Whether the cause initially looks accidental, incendiary, or natural, it is important to look at all the data gathered with an open mind and not formulate opinions until all evidence has been collected and examined and all reasonable hypotheses have been tested. The fire cause is determined by identifying the heat, fuel, oxygen, and the event that brought them together, resulting in the fire. If there is not enough information or evidence to formulate and successfully test a hypothesis, the fire should be classified as undetermined. At this point, depending upon the complexity or nature of the incident, it may be necessary to call in a qualified fire investigator.

Figure 5.19 Heavy equipment without a spark arrestor on the exhaust pipe is a frequent cause of wildland fires. *Courtesy of NIFC.*

Figure 5.20 Hot fragments from railcar brake shoes can ignite a fire.

Chapter 6:
Firesetters

ARSON FIRE

REWARD

PAID FOR INFORMATION
LEADING TO THE ARREST
AND INDICTMENT OF
PERSON(S) RESPONSIBLE.

CALL
OKLAHOMA ARSON HOTLINE

IF YOU KNOW WHO DID THIS
CALL:

TULSA: 918-596-2776

OKC: 1-800-522-8666

WE WILL PAY YOU UP TO $500.00 FOR ANY
INFORMATION WHICH LEADS TO THE ARREST AND
PROSECUTION OF PERSON(S) RESPONSIBLE.
ALL CALLS ARE HELD IN STRICT CONFIDENCE.

Courtesy of Donny Howard, Yates & Associates.

Job Performance Requirements

This chapter provides information that will assist the reader in meeting the following performance requirements from NFPA 1021, *Fire Officer Professional Qualifications,* 2002 edition. Boldfaced portions of the standard are specifically addressed in this chapter.

Chapter 5 Fire Officer II

5.5 Inspection and Investigation

5.5.2 Determine the point of origin and preliminary cause of a fire, given a fire scene, photographs, diagrams, pertinent data and/or sketches, to determine if arson is suspected.

> **(A) Requisite Knowledge. Methods used by arsonists,** common causes of fire, basic cause and origin determination, fire growth and development, and documentation of preliminary fire investigative procedures.

Chapter 6
Firesetters

Professional investigators and psychologists have studied multiple fire scenes and interviewed hundreds of arrested and convicted arsonists over many years to identify common motivation and to establish profiles. A *motive* is a reason or an incentive for an action (setting a fire), and firesetter profiles span all ages from adults to children.

Not all firesetters are arsonists. Children often imitate what they see their parents do **(Figure 6.1)**. Put this together with their natural curiosity, and the potential for the child to start a fire is significant. For example, a child sees his parents lighting a cigarette with a lighter. The child then plays with a lighter and catches his bedroom on fire. It was the child's natural curiosity that led him to start the fire. The fire investigator is the first link in preventing this from happening again by determining that this was the cause of the fire.

This chapter focuses on the categories of juvenile and adult firesetters and the reasons why they start fires. Understanding the broad categories of arson motivation and the reasons for juvenile firesetting may help the investigator to identify the firesetter by recognizing the manner and location in which a fire is set. With a sound intervention program, some juveniles can be helped and their firesetter behavior stopped through counseling and education.

Juveniles

Juvenile firesetters have become nationally recognized as a significant contributor to the U.S. residential fire problem. Children involved in firesetting account for more than one-third of all the fires set in the United States. In its publication *Crime in the United States, Uniform Crime Reports*, the FBI statistics show that in 1995, arrestees under age 18

Figure 6.1 Children often start fires because they have seen their parents using matches or cooking.

accounted for 42 percent of all arson arrests.

Juvenile firesetters are divided into five categories:

- Curiosity
- Crisis
- Delinquent
- Strategic
- Pathological

Curiosity Firesetters

Motivation for the curiosity firesetter is best described in the name. These children set fires that are not extremely complex. The most common ignition sources they use are lighters, matches, and accessible materials. Often, curiosity firesetters choose a secret area to begin a fire, believing that they will not be discovered (**Figure 6.2**). Closets, garages, or under the bed are well-known refuges of these children. Hiding may be the result of previous attempts by adults to limit the child's use of fire. This type of firesetting may or may not be limited to one episode. A lack of adult supervision combined with the availability of materials to ignite creates an atmosphere conducive to this firesetting behavior.

Figure 6.2 The child who is curious to see how fire behaves is likely to use something readily available, like matches or a lighter.

The curiosity firesetter may be characterized as difficult or even manipulative. It is likely that these firesetters have difficulty controlling their impulses and often learn by touching or doing things. They might be described as mechanically inclined. After setting the fire, the child may try to extinguish it or may run to tell adults. Although the children may not be aware of the consequences of setting fires, they may be guilty or ashamed of their actions.

This category of juvenile firesetters is populated by the youngest of firesetters. Curiosity firesetting may begin at three or four years of age and may be seen in those as old as twelve. Most, however, are less than seven years of age.

Crisis Firesetters

The crisis firesetter most often sets fires in response to stressful circumstances. The crisis firesetter may be reacting to circumstances in the home and may need attention because of family difficulties such as a single-parent home, recent divorce, recent addition of a sibling, etc. The crisis firesetter may set the fire at a location associated with the stress. For example, a crisis firesetter may light a fire in a schoolroom in response to a lack of acceptance from peers at school. The crisis firesetter may also use materials related to the stress; for example, the firesetter may feel left out when others are better at sports and use the sports equipment as the fuel of choice (**Figure 6.3**). These fires, like those of the curiosity firesetter, are relatively simple fires.

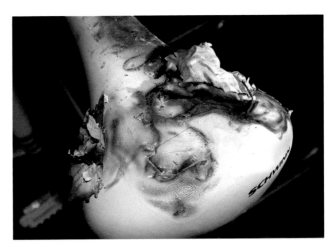

Figure 6.3 The child who is acting due to a crisis may set fire to play or sports equipment. *Courtesy of Bonnie Hudlet.*

Most crisis firesetters are reacting to a recent crisis. Some, although not all, have a history of abuse or neglect. Unable to express the feelings resulting from the stress or without someone to listen, such juveniles may set fires as a means of release. Because the juvenile may feel that fireset-

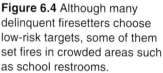
Figure 6.4 Although many delinquent firesetters choose low-risk targets, some of them set fires in crowded areas such as school restrooms.

ting was the only way to react, most do not display guilt. Frequently the crisis firesetter denies responsibility. This activity is often a shock to the parents who may not have been aware of the underlying stress.

Delinquent Firesetters

While curiosity firesetters are typically young children, delinquent firesetting is almost exclusively committed by older children. These firesetters are often described as irresponsible and resistant to authority. Many have academic troubles, and attention deficit disorder is common. These firesetters are often led into trouble by friends.

Delinquent firesetters primarily work in groups, frequently using accessible accelerants. Fires may be set in brush, along fences, trash cans, or other outdoor areas where the risk to others is perceived

to be low. An exception to the perceived low risk to others is fires set in school restrooms or trash cans **(Figure 6.4)**. The activities of delinquent firesetters are not limited to setting damaging fires. They may turn in false alarms or light smoke bombs or fireworks. Most often, this is done in the absence of close parental supervision.

The parents of these firesetters will often allow help from mental health professionals -- many have looked for assistance before. They may believe that law enforcement is not needed. The child will likely deny responsibility.

Strategic Firesetters

Strategic firesetters are often teenagers who are "streetwise" and who have a history of juvenile delinquency. Often, these firesetters have low self-esteem and find their support in peer groups that include gangs. These firesetters usually do not have strong scholastic records and are sometimes dropouts.

While the characteristics of the delinquent and strategic firesetters closely resemble each other, the motive and method of firesetting differs greatly. Strategic firesetters act with the intent to damage property and/or cause harm. The fires are similar to the adult revenge fire; accelerants and multiple points of origin are common **(Figure 6.5)**. Sometimes the strategic firesetter may also be motivated by crime concealment.

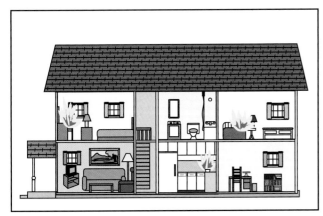

Figure 6.5 Because strategic firesetters act with the desire to cause damage, they often set fires that have multiple areas of origin.

Strategic firesetting is extremely prevalent among gangs and other groups with codes of silence. Cities plagued by gang fires indicate that the Molotov cocktail is the ignition source of choice. These firesetters have no regard for the law and may even boast about their fires.

Pathological Firesetters

These firesetters are characterized by recurring firesetting behavior. A history of physical or psychological disorders is common and, again, the child may not be successful in school. Even so, pathological firesetters may be extremely intelligent. Frequently they are victims of emotional trauma including abuse or neglect.

The fires set by the pathological firesetter may be sophisticated and are almost always destructive. Accelerants and multiple points of origin are commonplace. A strong tie is made between the family environment and this type of firesetting.

In addition to an abusive family setting, substance abuse by the firesetter's parents has been tied to pathological firesetters. In number, this is the smallest group of juvenile firesetters.

Intervention

The juvenile firesetting problem is a serious concern. This drives the need for organizations to develop methods to address the problem and to counsel the juvenile firesetter. Fire department officials are often the first to become aware of the juvenile firesetter and, without an intervention process, may find themselves ill-equipped to handle the situation. Fire department intervention programs should not replace trained, credentialed, mental health professionals in those cases where psychological abnormalities may be contributing to the firesetting behavior. Fire department personnel should work closely with the juvenile court system, juvenile probation office, police department, and local counseling services to set up juvenile firesetter programs.

Children who become firesetters typically do not stop without intervention. Although the juvenile firesetter problem may be best addressed through the educational efforts of the school system, a fire department intervention program may provide extra assistance in counseling that could prove beneficial **(Figure 6.6, p.69)**.

The juvenile firesetter program should be organized in such a manner as to work with community organizations in a cooperative effort to modify and correct juvenile behavior. The assistance of community organizations can reduce the number of juvenile-involved fires, creating a safer community without a substantial financial burden.

Adults

An adult who intentionally (or knowingly) and maliciously sets a fire is categorized as an "arsonist." The types of fires and the motives for setting the fires are varied; however, documented studies by professionals provide generalizations that assist in identifying the underlying reasons why the fire was set.

Figure 6.6 Educational efforts that are coordinated between the fire department and schools are designed to promote fire safety.

Motives

Adult firesetters are usually motivated by revenge, vandalism, profit (fraud), crime concealment, excitement (vanity), or extremism (terrorism). Fires are generally set in a location and manner unique to a specific motive. Identification of the motive provides valuable assistance in the identification of the party responsible for setting the fire.

Revenge

Fires set because of personal or professional vendettas fall into the largest category of arson fires and account for 50 percent of the total arson problem. Generally, the victim is able to provide information regarding the suspect's identity. Personal property is often the target, and ignitable liquids are seldom used because most often the fire is not "mapped out," but rather it occurs without planning and in reaction to an incident. Typical targets are vehicles, storage rooms or outbuildings, and fences (**Figure 6.7**). Fires set to homes or businesses are often set to the exterior or through a broken window. Molotov cocktails or "firebombs" may also be employed.

Revenge fires set in homes as a result of a spouse believed to be unfaithful are often set to that person's clothing or to the bed. Often a history of domestic disputes precedes the fire.

Figure 6.7 Lighter fluid was used to start a fire in this storage room. Note the splash pattern on the door. *Courtesy of Donny Howard, Yates and Associates.*

Vandalism

Vandalism fires are most often set by two or more individuals (usually juveniles) for no apparent reason other than "just for kicks." Schools are prime targets, and other common locations include vacant buildings, trash containers, and vegetation (**Figure 6.8, p. 70**). Forced entry to buildings is

Figure 6.8 Vacant buildings like this are prime targets for vandals.

present, and property damage and graffiti are often done before the fire.

Profit (Fraud)

Monetary gain is the primary motivator for this type of fire, and total destruction of property is the ultimate goal. The key to this fire is the desire to cause the most damage in the least possible time **(Figure 6.9)**. For that reason, multiple fires and ignitable liquids are common. Holes broken in the walls or ceilings, trailers, etc., are often used to assist in spreading the fire, and time-delay ignition devices are not uncommon. Fires set by the property owners are often elaborate in nature and require a significant setup time. No other motive allows a firesetter unlimited access and time to the interior of a structure without fear of discovery.

Personal property that cannot easily be replaced and pets are often removed before the fire. The property owner is frequently absent from the building and doors are found locked. Fraud fires are typically set because of poor financial status; however, the motivation for arson for profit may be quite abstract and as varied as the imagination of the firesetter. An example would include a profitable and well-established business set on fire for alternative fraud reasons; that is, a successful nightclub needs to be remodeled because of worn carpet and tobacco-smoked ceilings. If the owner were to close for the week required to complete the remodeling, revenue would be lost. If a fire was set to a business with adequate insurance, the overhead expenses, lost revenues, and remodeling fees would be paid through the business interruption insurance (if the fire were not properly investigated).

Other reasons for fraud fires do not involve the property owners. The fires are generally not elaborate and if set to the interior, require the firesetter to force entry. Examples of fires set for economic gain and not involving the owners or insured may include:

Figure 6.9 Flammable liquids were used to damage several areas in this store. *Courtesy of Donny Howard, Yates and Associates.*

- Competitors seeking to drive the victim out of business
- Contractors desiring to secure a contract for rebuilding the loss
- Insurance agents who wish to sell insurance to uninsured persons in the area
- Persons wishing to devalue the property so they can purchase it at a lower price
- Firefighters, security personnel, and law enforcement officers seeking overtime or call-out pay

Crime Concealment

Fire used as a tool to destroy evidence of another crime is most generally associated with burglary, homicide, and embezzlement **(Figure 6.10)**. The attempt to cover a burglary is most common with the fire set where evidence such as fingerprints or blood is believed to have been left. Most often the location is at the point of entry or where an item has been removed. The fire is generally set with combustibles on hand and rarely involves ignitable liquids because a burglar usually enters a structure with the intent to steal and not to set a fire. The fire is set after entry and after it is decided that incriminating evidence was "left behind."

Figure 6.10 Fires are frequently set during robberies. *Courtesy of Donny Howard, Yates and Associates.*

Homicide concealment fires, on the other hand, often involve the use of ignitable liquids in an attempt to destroy the body and any evidence of the manner and cause of death. These fires are generally set on and around the body.

Embezzlement fires are set to erase or destroy a "paper trail"; therefore, the paperwork and surrounding area are the origin for the fire. Often the paperwork itself is used as the fuel with ignitable liquids sometimes used to assist in the destruction of the documents.

Excitement (Vanity)

Excitement and action accompany a fire, and the ability to create a situation requiring the response of the fire service and law enforcement provide some people a feeling of empowerment over society. The spur-of-the-moment fires, however, develop a recognizable pattern over a period of time. Examples of pattern development include:

- **Dates and day of the week.** Paydays, normal work days, or days spent consuming alcohol are believed to help stimulate these individuals in firesetting.
- **Time of day.** The time of day or night may correspond with travel to and from work or other activity. Most excitement fires are set during the hours of darkness.
- **Type of structure.** The arsonist is often consciously or subconsciously attracted to a certain type of structure — for example, schools, churches, vacant structures, etc. **(Figures 6.11 a and b, p. 72)**.
- **How the fire is set.** The arsonist rarely plans to set a fire; therefore, combustibles on hand are most often used. They often become "comfortable" with a certain method and tend to stay with the method that has worked in the past.
- **Where the fire is set.** The arsonist tends to set these fires in similar locations (for example, under a crawl space) because prior fires set in this manner resulted in the desired emergency response and lack of detection.

Arsonists who seek recognition or who wish to be viewed as heroes may set and "discover" fires. These individuals are always present at the fire scene and often attempt to assist in fire fighting

Figures 6.11 a and b The arsonist may develop a pattern of setting fires to certain structures, like this vacant warehouse and church. *Courtesy of Joseph J. Marino.*

activities. They may be from any background; however, it has been noted that some have been employed as security guards, firefighters, and law enforcement officers. These same individuals may be seen at multiple fire scenes. If their presence is observed, the investigator should check their background for past examples of firesetting behavior.

Extremism (Terrorism)

Social protest by an individual or group may target a government, ethnic, or religious group or a facility that operates in opposition to their "cause" **(Figure 6.12)**. Fires or explosions are carried out with the intent to advertise or advance the arsonist's purpose. Although the arsonist wishes his or her individual identity to remain unknown, it is important that their group or "cause" be identified as

Figure 6.12 Incendiary fires that result from hatred or social protest are often accompanied by signs or graffiti.

the responsible party. Graffiti or signs may be left at the scene and phone calls or letters to the press are common. Fires and explosives are most often set to the exterior of buildings or are propelled (by a Molotov cocktail, for example) into the interior through broken windows or doorways.

Pyromania

Pyromania has not been included as a motive because it is a mental state and related to a psychological disorder. True pyromaniacs are few in number and set fires as a release of tension or in response to "voices" from within or in the form of an imaginary person or animal. These fires are seldom set with ignitable liquids and are often set to paper products in vehicles, alleys, or behind buildings. Over a short period of time it is common for this type of individual to set multiple small fires within several blocks of each other.

Summary

Firesetters can be categorized as juveniles or adults and each category can be subdivided into more specific categories. The juvenile category is subdivided into curiosity, crisis, delinquent, strategic, and pathological firesetters. These firesetters may be helped through specific types of intervention — from educational to psychological counseling. Adult categories include the motives behind the firesetting. These include revenge, vandalism, profit (fraud), crime concealment, excitement (vanity), and extremism (terrorism). Fire department personnel are not expected to be experts in the psychological profiles of firesetters. However, if the investigator is familiar with the firesetter categories and the characteristics of each, he or she may be able to provide essential information to prevent accidental fires and to apprehend and prosecute those responsible for arson fires.

Chapter 7:
Preserving Physical Scene Evidence

Job Performance Requirements

This chapter provides information that will assist the reader in meeting the following performance requirements from NFPA 1001, *Fire Fighter Professional Qualifications,* 2002 edition. Boldfaced portions of the standard are specifically addressed in this chapter.

Chapter 6 Fire Fighter II

6.2 Fire Department Communications

6.2.1 Complete a basic incident report, given the report forms, guidelines, and information, so that all pertinent information is recorded, the information is accurate, and the report is complete.

(A) **Requisite Knowledge.** Content requirements for basic incident reports, **the purpose and useful-ness of accurate reports, consequences of inaccurate reports, how to obtain necessary information,** and required coding procedures.

6.3 Fireground Operations

6.3.4* Protect evidence of fire cause and origin, given a flashlight and overhaul tools, so that the evidence is noted and protected from further disturbance until investigators can arrive on the scene.

(A) **Requisite Knowledge.** Methods to assess origin and cause; types of evidence; means to protect various types of evidence; the role and relation-ship of Fire Fighter IIs, criminal investigators, and insurance investigators in fire investigations; and the effects and problems associated with removing property or evidence from the scene.

(B) **Requisite Skills.** The ability to locate the fire's origin area, recognize possible causes, and protect the evidence.

A.6.3.4 The Fire Fighter II should be able to recognize important evidence as to a fire's cause and maintain the evidence so that further testing can be done without contamination or chain-of-custody problems. Evidence should be left in place (when possible, oth-erwise chain-of-custody must be established), not altered by improper handling, walking, and so forth, and not destroyed. Possible means to protect evidence is to avoid touching, protect with salvage covers during overhaul, or rope off the area where the evidence lies. The Fire Fighter II is not intended to be highly proficient at origin and cause determination.

Jurisdictions that use Fire Fighter IIs to determine origin and cause should comply with the requirements of NFPA 1021, *Standard for Fire Officer Professional Qualifica-tions.*

Emergency Responder Guidelines

This chapter provides information that will assist the reader in meeting the following first responder guidelines for fire ser-vice, law enforcement, and emergency medical personnel from the Office for Domestic Preparedness (ODP) Emergency Responder Guidelines, 2002 Edition.

ODP Emergency Responder Guidelines

Fire Service, Law Enforcement, and Emergency Medical personnel

Awareness Level for Events Involving Weapons of Mass Destruction

(**NOTE:** The skills listed are applicable to emergency scenes that may involve arson.)

IV. Know procedures for protecting a potential crime scene. The law enforcement officer should:

a. **Understand and implement procedures for pro-tecting evidence and minimizing disturbance of the potential crime scene while protecting others.** Understand the roles, responsibilities, and jurisdictions of Federal agencies related to a WMD event or incident.

b. Recognize the importance of crime scene preser-vation and initiate measures to secure the scene.

c. **Protect physical evidence such as footprints, relevant containers, or wrapping paper, etc.**

d. **Advise witnesses and bystanders who may have information to remain at the scene in a safe location until they have been interviewed and released. Be aware of people arriving or departing the scene. Note license plate numbers or other relevant data. Question the caller, witness(es), or victim(s) to obtain criti-cal information regarding the incident or event.** Such questions include, "Where is the package, and what does it contain?" "Does the package have an unusual odor or smell?" "Has the package been disturbed?" "Have there been any threats received before receipt of the package" "Does the package contain a written threat, and if so, what does it say?"

Chapter 7
Preserving Physical Fire Scene Evidence

The emergency response personnel at a fire scene are most likely to discover the initial evidence that may later be relevant to a fire investigation. Therefore, they must know how to recognize, document, and preserve evidence for the person who investigates the incident. This chapter focuses on the proper techniques for collecting and preserving evidence to maintain its integrity. Preservation of evidence starts at the time of the initial report and may include the entire fire scene. **The entire fire scene should be considered evidence; therefore, such actions as moving objects should be kept to an absolute minimum.** The chapter also explains the importance of maintaining a record of the chain of custody of the evidence collected. The chain of custody must be traceable from the time evidence is found until it is presented in the courtroom. The chapter concludes with a discussion of how to document the investigation through the use of sketches and photographs.

Types of Evidence

Generally, evidence is any means of proof that may be presented to prove or disprove a certain matter. Evidence is usually used to support testimony but can sometimes speak for itself. Three primary categories of evidence are direct, circumstantial, and physical.

Direct evidence is composed of those facts to which a person can attest without further support. Direct evidence is found through the five physical senses. Examples of direct evidence are a person *seeing* (witnessing) another individual pour and ignite gasoline on a floor or observing a coffeemaker erupt into flames. Another example is someone *smelling* propane odors in a structure.

Circumstantial evidence is that which supports an inference formed from direct evidence. For example, one could infer that a person set a fire in a building if there was direct evidence that the person was seen carrying a container of ignitable liquid into the building and was seen running from the building as the fire started. One could also infer that a smoldering cigarette started a fire noticed shortly after an ashtray has been emptied into a trash receptacle.

A common misconception concerning circumstantial evidence is that it is not as valuable as direct evidence. Both criminal prosecutions and civil litigation traditionally rely heavily on circumstantial evidence. On occasion, cases may be proven using only circumstantial evidence because direct evidence may not be available.

Another form of evidence is known as *physical* or *real evidence* and includes physical objects available for inspection. Following are some examples of physical (real) evidence that may relate to fire cases **(Figures 7.1 a - c, p. 106)**:

- Electrical conductors
- Photographs, film, tape recordings or videotapes
- Gas can
- Closed sprinkler valve or other disabled device
- Fire patterns
- Footware impressions
- Lack of something expected, such as empty closets
- Warning labels and owners' manuals
- Damaged gas piping
- Appliances

Figures 7.1 a - c Physical evidence can be inspected and photographed. Such items as burned switch boxes, warning labels, and the remains of appliances may give important clues to the origin of the fire. *Courtesy of Donny Howard, Yates & Associates.*

Admissibility of Evidence

The ERP at the scene are not in a position to decide whether the evidence they find will be admissible in court; therefore, they should collect, document, and preserve all possible evidence. It is better to preserve too much evidence than not enough, so every piece of evidence should be treated as though it is significant. If ERPs must move an object of evidence, they should photograph it, document its position and location, and tag it before removal. ERPs should never move or disturb any evidence before the arrival of the investigator unless it is absolutely necessary to protect it from damage.

Spoliation

Emergency services personnel should exercise caution during and after fire fighting operations to avoid spoliating evidence. The term *spoliation* refers to the act of losing, destroying, or altering evidence (or potential evidence) found at the fire scene. **It is the responsibility of ERPs and investigators who may handle such evidence to preserve it and avoid its destruction.** Every effort should be made to photograph, document, and preserve any evidence prior to moving it from the location in which it was found. Any destructive testing of fire scene evidence requires advance notification to all reasonably known interested parties who may wish to participate in or monitor the testing.

ERPs must be aware that spoliation can result in monetary sanctions, dismissal of a defense or claim, exclusion of expert testimony, and prosecution under statutes relating to obstruction of justice. It is vitally important that all emergency response personnel be aware of the actions and procedures needed to avoid spoliation of potential evidence. NFPA 921, *Guide for Fire and Explosion Investigation,* offers definitions and guidelines for personnel who must handle and document evidence.

NOTE: Refer to the entire standard for further information.

NFPA 921 Guidelines on Spoliation

A few of the basics of this standard are as follows:

11.3.5 Spoliation of Evidence. Spoliation of evidence refers to the loss, destruction, or material alteration of an object or document that is evidence or potential evidence in a legal proceeding by one who has the responsibility for its preservation. Spoliation of evidence may occur when the movement, change, or destruction of evidence, or the alteration of the scene significantly impairs the opportunity of other interested parties to obtain the same evidentiary value from the evidence, as did any prior investigator.

11.3.5.1 Responsibility. The responsibility of the investigator (or anyone who handles or examines evidence) for evidence preservation, and the scope of that responsibility varies based on such factors as the jurisdiction, whether the investigator is a public official or private sector investigator, whether criminal conduct is indicated, and applicable laws and regulations. However, regardless of the scope and responsibility of the investigation, care should be taken to avoid destruction of evidence.

11.3.5.2 Documentation. Efforts to photograph, document, or preserve evidence should apply not only to evidence relevant to an investigator's opinions, but also to evidence of reasonable alternate hypotheses that were considered and ruled out.

11.3.5.3 Remedies for Spoliation. Criminal and civil courts have applied various remedies when there has been spoliation of evidence. Remedies employed by the courts may include discovery sanctions, monetary sanctions, application of evidentiary inferences, limitations under the rules of evidence, exclusion of expert testimony, dismissal of a claim or defense, independent tort actions for the intentional or negligent destruction of evidence, and even prosecution under criminal statutes relating to obstruction of justice. Investigators should conduct their investigations so as to minimize the loss or destruction of evidence and thereby to minimize allegations of spoliation.

Guidance regarding notification can be found in ASTM E 860, Standard Practice for Examining and Testing Items That Are or May Become Involved in Products Liability Litigation, and ASTM E 1188, Standard Practice for Collection and Preservation of Information and Physical Items by a Technical Investigator. Guidance for labeling of evidence can be found in ASTM E 1459, Standard Guide for Physical Evidence Labeling and Related Documentation.

Documenting Information

It is important that the ERP investigating the fire record accurate and concise notes (**Figure 7.2**). Note taking should include factual information relating to the incident. Do not include personal opinions with the notes; remember that they may need to be used in legal proceedings. There are several methods for taking notes, the most common of which are hand-writing and voice-recording. Notes are also useful in the preparation of accurate reports.

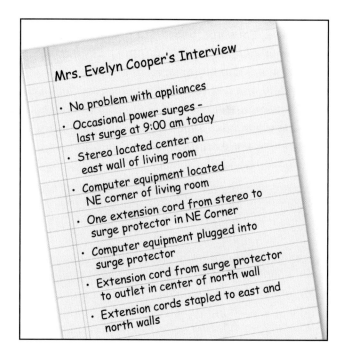

Figure 7.2 Make sure that notes are factual, complete, and neatly written so they can be used in a fire investigation.

Chain of Custody

When dealing with physical evidence, keeping the integrity of the "chain of custody" is of prime importance. Document every second of the evidence's existence from the time it is found until it is presented in court. Every person who has had possession of the evidence must be able to attest to the fact that the evidence has not been contaminated or altered. The investigator, who may be the chief witness in court, must be able to state the location and time the evidence was located and collected.

Upon their arrival, ERPs should take the following steps to collect, document, and preserve evidence at the fire scene:

Step 1: Secure the scene and keep unnecessary people out of the area.

Step 2: Preserve the evidence that is in danger of destruction in the best possible way.

Step 3: Photograph the evidence in place. In addition, mark and label the location of the evidence on the fire scene sketch **(Figures 7.3 a - c)**.

Step 4: Note the time the evidence was discovered, where it was discovered, and the name of the person who made the discovery.

Step 5: Maintain and secure the area against unauthorized entry, including other ERPs, while the evidence is in its original position or until it is collected. When it is necessary to move the evidence, ERP should record the time and the name of the person removing the evidence. Evidence should be moved to a secure location that can only be accessed by authorized personnel.

Preservation of Physical Evidence

ERPs can use an evidence kit when there is a need to preserve evidence for the investigator. The components of such a kit should be of professional quality, kept in a locked toolbox, and used only for investigation purposes **(Figure 7.4)**. It may include the following items:

- Pencil and paper
- Chain-of-custody forms **(Figure 7.5)**
- Tire-tread-depth gauge
- New, unused, lab-approved metal cans -- paint cans with metal lids that can be sealed (obtainable directly from the manufacturer); canning jars with sealable lids **(Figures 7.6 a and b)**
- Plastic protectors for sheets of paper
- Small evidence boxes
- Small glass vials with a cotton swab in each

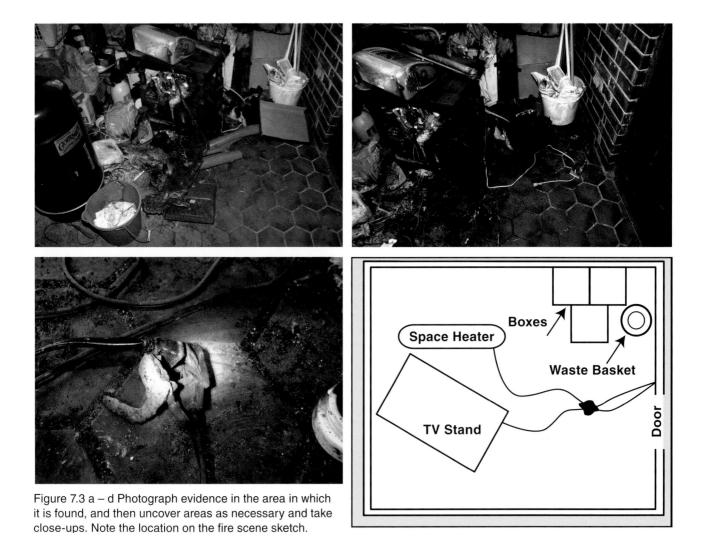

Figure 7.3 a – d Photograph evidence in the area in which it is found, and then uncover areas as necessary and take close-ups. Note the location on the fire scene sketch.
Courtesy of Donny Howard, Yates & Associates.

Figure 7.4 The evidence kit must be kept locked. *Courtesy of Donny Howard, Yates & Associates.*

CHAIN OF CUSTODY FORM

Incident Number. . . . .

Date of Incident. . . . . . . Time. . . . . .a.m./p.m.

Search Officer. . . . .

Evidence Description . . . .

. . . .

Location. . . . .

. . . .

CHAIN OF CUSTODY

Received From. . . . .

By. . . . .

Date. . . . . Time. . . . . a.m./p.m.

Received From. . . . .

By. . . . .

Date. . . . . Time. . . . . a.m./p.m.

Received From. . . . .

By. . . . .

Date. . . . . Time. . . . . a.m./p.m.

Figures 7.6 a and b Evidence kits should include such items as clean paint cans with sealable lids, disposable gloves, cameras and film, tools for removing evidence, and plastic containers. *Courtesy of Donny Howard, Yates & Associates.*

Figure 7.5 Chain of custody forms are crucial for noting that evidence has been properly tagged and saved.

- Plastic evidence bags
- Paper envelopes or bags of various sizes
- Utility knife
- Flashlight
- Absorbent pads
- Putty knife and tablespoon for collecting samples
- Carbide-tipped metal scriber for marking evidence containers
- Felt-tipped permanent marking pens
- Evidence tags and labels with pressure-sensitive adhesive
- 50- or 100-foot steel-measuring tape
- Disposable rubber or latex gloves

- Quality camera(s) and supplies (memory cards or film)
- Filter masks
- Square-point shovel
- Broom (whisk, corn)
- Coveralls
- 6- or 12-inch ruler **(Figures 7.7 a and b)**
- Hand cleaner and paper towels
- Rake
- Common hand tools (for example, screwdriver and pliers)

Delegate one person to collect and tag all evidence. The investigator may have difficulty coordinating the case if more than one person has collected evidence. For example, if a piece of evidence must be collected by a person other than the one assigned, the evidence still must be properly contained, marked, and given to the responsible person as soon as possible **(Figure 7.8)**.

The person delegated to collect and tag evidence must also keep a log of all evidence collected **(Figure 7.9)**. Both the evidence tag and log may include the following:

- Date, time, and specific location of discovery
- Name of the finder
- Name of the person removing the evidence from the scene
- Description of the evidence
- Evidence item number (simply 1, 2, 3, etc.)
- Incident name or number

Fire suppression forces should preserve evidence when it is found and provide security for the area until an investigator arrives. They should not gather or handle evidence unless it is absolutely necessary in order to preserve it. If a firefighter handles or procures evidence, he or she then becomes a link in the custody chain. The firefighter

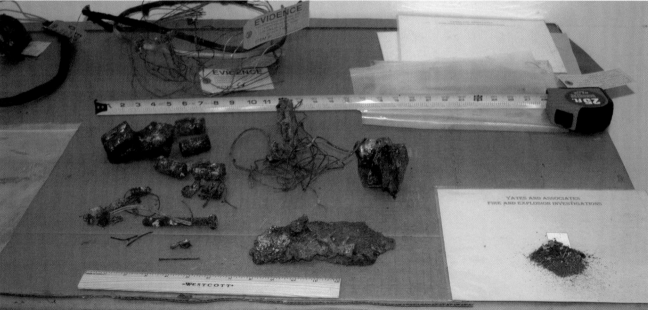

Figures 7.7 a and b Use the rulers and measuring tapes in the evidence kit to show the size of evidence and its relation to other objects. *Courtesy of Donny Howard, Yates & Associates.*

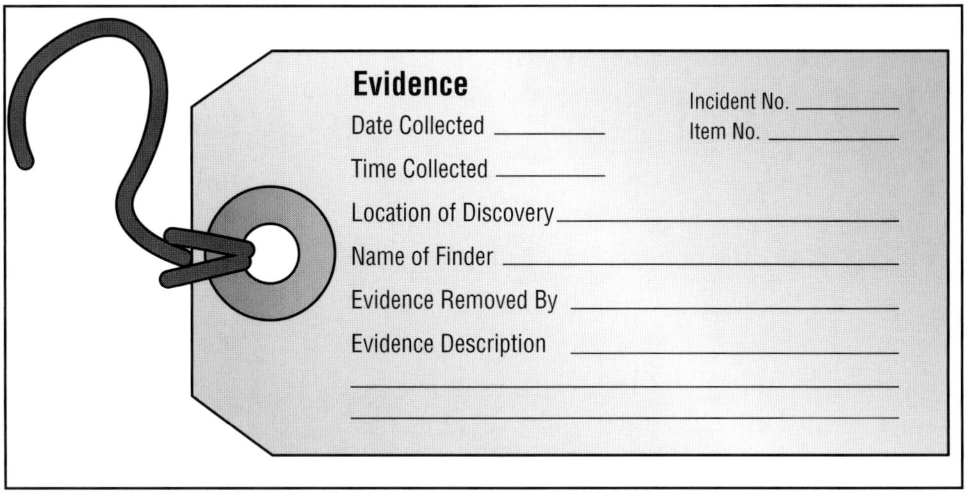

Figure 7.8 Make sure that all ERPs fill out evidence tags completely.

Evidence

Date Collected _____

Time Collected _____

Location of Discovery _____

Name of Finder _____

Evidence Removed By _____

Evidence Description _____

_____

_____

Incident No. _____

Item No. _____

Figure 7.9. Use evidence logs to document important information about evidence before it is moved.

Evidence Log

Incident #____120____

Item #	Date	Time	Location	Finder	Removed By
01	3/31/04	0430	S/W side of house	T. Bennett	D. Smith
02	3/31/04	0500	Outside S/W entrance	S. Robinson	D. Smith
03	3/31/04	0513	S/E corner of living room	D. Smith	D. Smith
04	3/31/04	0515	Living room into bedroom	T.Bennett	D. Smith
05	3/31/04	0600	West side of living room	D. Smith	D. Smith

should accurately document all actions as soon as possible. It may be necessary for this individual to subsequently appear in court.

It is very important that ERPs avoid the temptation to finish with an incident scene too quickly in order to return to regular duties. The need to remain on scene can be especially burdensome when an emergency occurs in extreme conditions, such as the middle of the night in inclement weather and the ERPs are cold and tired. Nonetheless, properly securing the scene and preserving the chain of custody are crucial to any potential investigation, so it is vital that these duties be performed even under the worst of conditions.

Handle evidence carefully when moving it. Techniques should be employed to prevent cross-contamination. For example, before handling certain types of evidence, it might be advisable to wear a clean pair of disposable, latex, or rubber gloves. Check with your department for guidelines for handling evidence. The following lists the types of evidence and the suggested procedures for handling each:

The evidence collector should consider changing latex gloves as well as cleaning the collection tools between each sample gathered.

Pieces of glass or bottles

- Pick up broken glass carefully to save potential fingerprints. When picking up the glass, place fingers only at the edges of the glass (**Figure 7.10**).

- Pick up a bottle by inserting a finger into the neck or by gripping the upper extremity of the neck.

- Put glass exhibits in a warm, dry place and stand them upright.

- Do not wrap the object in a handkerchief — any fingerprints will be smudged.

- Use paper bags or envelopes rather than plastic for storage.

Figure 7.10 Pick up glass by handling it carefully at the edges.

Ash and common fire debris

Seal ash and other debris in an unused, airtight metal can or glass container.

Liquid containers

- Handle liquid containers carefully; the heat of a fire does not necessarily destroy fingerprints.

- Handle the containers only on the edges or corners and not on flat surfaces where fingerprints may be present. Seal these containers in metal or paper containers (**Figure 7.11**). Empty plastic containers (even if melted) may contain residue that can be identified through laboratory analysis; therefore, seal them in a proper container as well.

Figure 7.11 Make sure that liquid containers are sealed in metal or paper containers.

Unidentified liquids

- Place liquid samples into clean, unused metal cans, glass vials, or special evidence bags (**Figure 7.12**).

- Do not use ordinary plastic bags or containers that have plastic lids because hydrocarbons will usually destroy or permeate ordinary plastic.

- After collecting a liquid sample, place a clean, unused cotton swab from the same box into an empty vial, and then seal and label the vial. The testing laboratory will use this vial as the comparison sample to prove that there was no contamination of the other vials. The laboratory does not need large quantities of liquid. Place a cotton swab, saturated with the suspect liquid, into a separate vial, and then seal and label this vial as well.

Figure 7.12 Place liquid samples into clean jars or cans and then seal them. *Courtesy of Donny Howard, Yates & Associates.*

Materials saturated with liquid

- Place items or materials suspected of being saturated with ignitable liquid in proper evidence containers. Absorbent material, such as carpet, cloth, or paper, may absorb ignitable liquids and can be good sample material.

- Do not overlook items such as concrete and soil as possible sample materials because they may also absorb ignitable liquids. Wood can also be taken as a sample but may not be as absorbent as some other materials **(Figure 7.13)**. Wood from protected areas, such as grooves between floorboards or behind baseboards, may be a better sample source.

Figure 7.14 Handle loose charred documents very carefully. Place them in containers as soon as possible. *Courtesy of Bonnie Hudlet.*

Figure 7.13 Wood can be taken as samples, even though it may not be as absorbent as other materials. *Courtesy of Donny Howard, Yates & Associates.*

Charred documents

- Leave charred documents found in containers such as wastebaskets, small file cabinets, and binders that can be moved easily.

- Handle loose charred documents very carefully, and keep away from drafts **(Figure 7.14)**.

Tire tracks or footprints

- Photograph from several angles, using side lighting. Place a ruler beside the tire tracks or footprints to show size relationships **(Figures 7.15 a and b)**. Be sure to include a general photograph of the print showing its location in relation to the rest of the area. If casts are to be made of tracks, protect the tracks with boxes or large pails until molds are completed **(Figure 7.16, p. 114)**.

NOTE: More information concerning the collection and preservation of evidence is listed in **Appendix C**.

Figures 7.15 a and b Photograph tire tracks from several angles to show a closeup and their relationship to the rest of the scene.

Figure 7.16 Cover footprints or tire tracks with a box to preserve them.

Evidence Checklist

The particular evidence and information that is collected at the scene is up to the judgment of the fire investigator. The following is a partial list of items of evidence and information the investigator may find.

- **Separate fires.** Signs of separate, unrelated fires in different locations and rooms.

- **Timing devices.** Cigarette-match combinations and candles are frequently used timing devices. Wax from a candle often soaks into the floor and can be detected on the scene or from a laboratory test. The spot beneath the candle often is not burned as badly as the surrounding floor. Alarm clocks are not often used as timing devices but should not be discounted. The metal parts of alarm clocks and similar devices are seldom destroyed by fire.

- **Trailers.** Trailers are used to spread the fire from one area of a structure to another or from one floor level to another (**Figures 7.17 a and b**). Trailers are usually ordinary combustibles, often soaked with ignitable liquids. Items used to make trailers may include:
  — Toilet paper
  — Newspapers
  — Black gunpowder
  — Wax paper
  — Excelsior
  — Blasting or hobby fuse
  — String
  — Rope
  — Cotton, paper, and similar materials

Figure 7.17 Note the concentrated patterns of damage that result when trailers are used to spread fire.

- **Chemicals.** Some examples are oxidizers such as swimming pool chlorine products, wood stain, and chemicals used in clandestine drug labs.

- **Matches.** Matches are not always consumed by the fire. Unburned matchbooks can be compared to a match found at the scene or may carry fingerprints; therefore, handle them carefully.

- **Ignitable liquids.** Flammable and combustible liquids include gasoline, kerosene, solvent, alcohol, paint thinner, acetone, ether, and others.

- **Bottles.** Bottles may be used to hold ignitable liquids such as those used to make Molotov cocktails. Unburned cloth might be found in the bottle's neck. Some remains of the bottle may be found (**Figure 7.18**).

- **Rubber items.** Condoms, toy balloons, hot-water bottles, and similar rubber items used to hold ignitable liquids or other flammable products (**Figure 7.19**).

Figure 7.18 The remains of a Molotov cocktail.

Figure 7.19 Balloons, condoms, and other similar items are often used to hold ignitable liquids.

- **Containers.** Other containers that could have held ignitable liquids can often be found in the structure or on the grounds around the structure.

- **Glass.** Glass that focused the sun's rays on a combustible substance may be recovered at the scene. This type of evidence may be more common in wildland fires than in structural fires.

- **Lighters.** The plastic container from a lighter may be consumed, but the metal portions of the lighter may still be located (**Figure 7.20, p. 116**).

- **Electrical sources.** There can be evidence of electrical heating appliances in contact with common combustibles; overloads on circuits can also be observed (**Figure 7.21, p. 116**).

- **Modified equipment.** Appliances, safety devices, fuel supplies, and other controls that have been tampered with or improperly repaired may malfunction.

- **Items present (that should not be there) and items missing (should be there but are not).** Examples of items present would include all of the physical evidence previously mentioned. Items missing may include clothes, firearms, baseball card collection, sentimental items, etc.

- **Oily rags.** The ash of an oily rag, tablecloth, or clothing may retain its shape and may be readily identifiable.

- **Fire patterns.** Fire patterns are physical evidence and should be documented (**Figure 7.22, p. 116**).

- **Common items.** Many common items can initiate a fire, either intentionally or accidentally.

Sketches and Diagrams

It may be helpful if the ERPs produce a sketch of the fire scene while the fire scene examination is conducted. The four basic types of sketches needed include a site plan, detailed floor plan, content diagram, and exploded sketch.

- **Site plan.** Shows the scene to include the structure and the grounds surrounding it and any other adjoining structures (**Figure 7.23, p. 116**).

- **Detailed floor plan.** Shows the floor plan of the entire structure and the actual location of the burned or damaged furnishings in their original positions before the fire. It may also include other pertinent information such as the location of evidence **(Figure 7.24)**.

- **Content diagram.** Shows the location and original position of the burned or damaged furnishings before the fire **(Figure 7.25)**.

- **Exploded sketch.** Shows a three-dimensional view (by folding sketch) of burn damage to the walls, floors, and ceilings. This sketch also can be used to show the location of photographs taken and sample collections **(Figure 7.26)**.

NOTE: Very large fire scenes may require the use of surveying equipment to document the scene and prepare sketches **(Figure 7.27, p. 118)**.

Figure 7.20 The metal parts of a lighter may still be detectable in the fire debris.

Figure 7.21 Note the evidence of electrical overload in this light fixture. *Courtesy of CT Office of State Fire Marshal.*

Figure 7.22 Analyzing fire patterns is very important in determining the cause of a fire. Photograph any such evidence. *Courtesy of Donny Howard, Yates & Associates.*

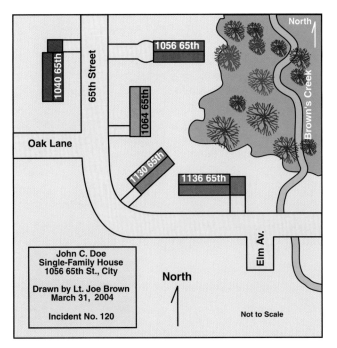

Figure 7.23 The site plan should provide an overview of the structure and surrounding area.

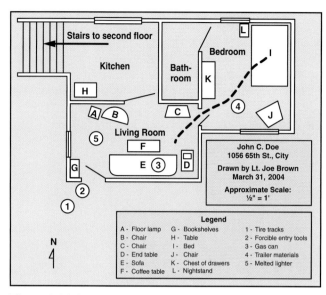

Figure 7.24 A sample detailed floor plan should include the floor plan and the furnishings as they are found. Evidence should be noted on the sketch.

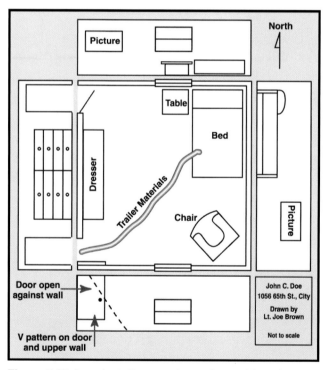

Figure 7.25 A content diagram shows the position of furnishings and burned materials.

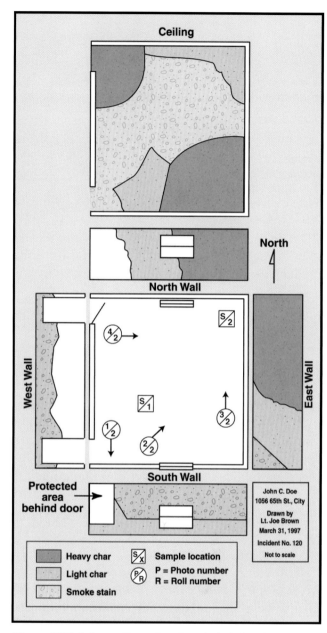

Figure 7.26 A three-dimensional exploded sketch.

Figure 7.27 A large fire scene may require the use of surveying equipment to document the fire area. *Courtesy of CT Office of State Fire Marshal.*

ERPs making the initial fire scene analysis may produce any of these sketches, depending on the situation and the estimated time of arrival of the investigator. Several good sketch-making kits on the market include preprinted grid paper and templates that make the sketching quicker and easier.

Measurements should be as accurate as possible. If there is no way to accurately measure distances with a tape, a person may use paces or steps. If distances are paced, indicate this method on the drawing. Triangulate measurements from two or more fixed points such as walls, door casings, pipes, electrical outlets, or anything else of relative permanence. The sketch maker should hold the measuring end of the tape and check both ends when necessary.

Additional guidelines for making sketches and maps include the following:

- Indicate directions (especially north).

- Keep the drawing simple by showing only pertinent points such as the area of origin and evidence of fire cause.

- Indicate the approximate measurement scale in one location on the page, preferably the lower-right corner. Do not put the actual measurements on the drawing.

- Indicate "not to scale" on sketch to avoid possible later challenges to exact sizes, etc., of items sketched.

- Use more than one drawing if more information needs to be illustrated.

- Indicate the date drawn, by whom, the fire scene location, and the file or incident number on each sketch. Include a legend indicating what each letter or number represents if this method is used.

- Identify furniture with letters of the alphabet; however, identify pieces of evidence with numerals.

- Do not try to fit too much detail into a small drawing. Make the drawing legible. Use more drawings or larger paper if necessary.

Photography

For a complete record of the fire scene, photographs during the fire are helpful, but are a necessity during the scene examination process. Diagrams and sketches show the objects in the area of their relative setting, but nothing else has the value of a photograph.

Many departments tend to avoid fire scene photography, believing that extensive and expensive equipment is necessary and that a professional photographer is needed to get useful photographs. Special lenses, filters, and lighting equipment can enhance photographs of the scene, but they are not necessities.

Many people use a Polaroid™ or similar "instant-print" camera for initial shots when immediacy is needed, and then they follow-up with a quality camera. ERPs should not, however, rely totally on "instant-print" photographs. The pictures lack detail, the print can fade, and there are no negatives for duplicates. Good, detailed, and usable photographs are very important. Any camera is better than no camera, but every fire department should have at least one quality camera and someone who has some skill in using it. Remember that burned areas of a structure are generally dark and may require a strong strobe or auxiliary lighting to produce usable photographs.

The important criterion to remember is that to be admissible in court, photographic prints must be an accurate and fair representation of the scene as the photographer observed it and as the scene was worked.

Photographic Record-Keeping (Photo Log)

It may be of assistance to make a record of each shot in a small notebook or on a portable tape recorder for later transcription **(Figure 7.28)**. For a more complete record, consider making a sketch of the scene and mark the spots from which each photograph was shot. As with all sketches, be sure to indicate the direction north.

Photography Guidelines

The rule of thumb is to photograph everything of importance and do so continually if possible during and certainly after the fire. This rule might seem to go a bit overboard, but it is not much of an overstatement. The photographer's goal is to tell a story with pictures **(Figures 7.29 a-c, p.120)**. If cost is a consideration, remember that film is relatively inexpensive, especially when compared to the cost in money and lives caused by needless accidental or intentional fires. Photographs, if used wisely, may help to reduce fire incidence. Fire scene pho-

Photograph Log

Roll No. _5_   Incident No. _120_   Date _3/31/04_

Frame	Location	Direction of Photo	Remarks
1	Main entrance door	North	Forcible entry marks on door
2	Living Room	Northeast	Trailer material
3	Bedroom	South	V pattern on door and upper wall

Figure 7.28 A photographic log is used to keep track of every photo and its relevance to the fire scene.

tographs are also helpful for post-fire critiques and for documenting operations (for example, making sketches of apparatus positions and layouts). Photographs can also be used for public relations purposes and training aids.

The photographs taken during the fire will be used later to corroborate or contradict statements concerning the fire, such as location and spread. Take photographs of the fire and fire structure as soon as possible. Other guidelines include the following:

- Take photographs of bystanders. Certain individuals may be present in photographs of bystanders at other emergency scenes.

- Take more shots as the fire progresses, spaced perhaps at five-, ten-, and fifteen-minute intervals.

- Take photographs on all sides of the building when possible.

- Take some photos from the vantage point of an aerial apparatus or from the windows or roof of a neighboring building if circumstances are favorable **(Figures 7.30 a and b, p.121)**.

After the fire is sufficiently suppressed and the safety of the scene is established, the photographer may move to the interior of the structure to photograph the fire and the operations. Most of the photographs of the scene are taken after the fire. Consider the following when taking photographs at the scene:

- Take both general area and specific shots.

- Work from the exterior to the interior and from areas of least damage to most damage.

Figures 7.29 a-c Exterior photographs not only document the fire scene but also help "tell the story" of the fire.

- Take general photographs of all exterior walls and then closer ones of windows and doors.
- Photograph each item of special interest immediately. Take one or more general photographs showing the item's relationship to the rest of the scene (**Figures 7.31 a and b, p.122**). Also take a close-up of the item and then another close-up including a legible measuring scale.
- Take similar general and specific before-and-after photographs if samples of any kind are collected or if anything is moved from its original location.
- Photograph all features inside the structure that can help tell the story of origin, cause, and spread. These include ceilings, walls, floors, doors, windows, and furniture.
- Photograph ceilings for the area of greatest fire intensity and walls for patterns and other indications of the fire's path (**Figures 7.32 a and b, p.123**).
- Photograph floors for evidence of trailers, ignitable liquid patterns, unusual charring, and indication of furniture placement.
- Photograph doors and windows to show evidence of forced entry, to document whether they were latched or locked, and to show charring.
- Photograph objects that have melted and point to the area of greatest heat. Some examples include candles, plastic ornaments and flowers, and lightbulbs.
- When possible, photograph evidence as it is being collected (**Figure 7.33, p.123).**
- Photograph objects of interest after they have been tagged (**Figures 7.34 a and b, p.123**).

Photographing Victims

The firefighter seldom has the duty of photographing bodies found at a fire scene, but there might be a time when it is necessary. The body and the location where it is found needs to be photographed both before and after it is moved. Photograph the immediate area around the victim with overlapping shots from all angles, showing the body's relationship to possible exits, the fire path and source, furniture placement, blocked exits and windows, and all things that appear to be out of the

Figures 7.30 a and b If possible, photograph a fire scene from several angles to give a more complete picture. *Courtesy of CT Office of State Fire Marshal.*

Figures 7.31 a and b After photographing items of special interest up close, show their relationship to the rest of the fire scene. *Courtesy of Donny Howard, Yates & Associates.*

Figure 7.33 In addition to photographing evidence, photograph it as it is being collected. *Courtesy of Donny Howard, Yates & Associates.*

Figures 7.32 a and b Be sure to photograph ceiling areas to show fire patterns and areas of greatest fire intensity. *Courtesy of Donny Howard, Yates & Associates.*

ordinary. Photograph all parts of the body as fire patterns may indicate the direction and intensity of the fire. If necessary, take more photographs at the hospital or mortuary where the body is taken or during the autopsy.

Summary

Although the ERP may not have to testify in a trial, the information gathered may be used in the courtroom. The facts and evidence the emergency services personnel gathered and the methods used to obtain them will be placed under close examination once they are entered into court. For this reason, the ERP must know the types of evidence to look for, proper methods of collection, and how to preserve and store the evidence once it has been collected. Documenting the scene through sketches, maps, and photographs is also very

Figures 7.34 a and b Photograph the tags after they are placed on evidence. *Courtesy of Donny Howard, Yates & Associates.*

important in substantiating any claims made in the case. Once the emergency services personnel has collected the evidence, sketched diagrams, and shot photographs of the area, he or she must also be able to trace the chain of custody of this evidence from the time it is found until it is presented in the courtroom.

Appendices

Courtesy of Donny Howard, Yates & Associates.

Appendix A
Organizations Interested in Fire Cause Determination

American Bar Association

Attorneys admitted to the bar of any state. Founded in 1878. Provides services, such as resources, materials, and professional review, to attorneys.

Address: 321 N. Clark Street, Chicago, IL 60610
Telephone: 312-988-5000

Web site: www.abanet.org

Battelle Memorial Institute Columbus Laboratories

Battelle attempts to meet the challenges of today in a broad range of research, educational, and invention and technology development activities. Its staff of 600 scientists, engineers, and supporting specialists bring their skills and training in the physical, life, and social-behavioral sciences to bear on the problems and needs of contemporary society. Founded in 1929.

Address: 505 King Avenue, Columbus, OH 43201-2693

Telephone: 614-424-6424

Web site: www.nbcindustrygroup.com/battel.htm

Consumer Product Safety Commission CPSC

The CPSC is committed to protecting consumers and families from products that pose a fire, electrical, chemical, or mechanical hazard or can injure children. The CPSC works to ensure the safety of consumer products such as toys, cribs, power tools, cigarette lighters, and household chemicals.

Mailing address: U.S. Consumer Product Safety Commission, Washington, D.C. 20207-0001
Street address: 4330 East-West Highway, Bethesda, MD 20814-4408

Telephone: 301-504-7923
Web site: www.cpsc.gov

Council of State Governments

Commissions on interstate cooperation, or similar bodies, in all 50 states and was established as official entities of state governments. Purposes are to serve governmental progress within the individual states, among the states working together, and by the states in their relations with the federal government. Founded in 1933.

Address: 2760 Research Park Drive, PO Box 11910, Lexington, KY 40578-1910

Telephone: 859-244-8000

Web site: www.csg.org

FM Global (Formerly Factory Mutual Research Corporation) (FM)

FM conducts research in property loss control, primarily to meet the needs of the Factory Mutual System. The information, however, is available for use by others. Data is gathered by testing, conducting surveys, and studies.

Address: FM Global Corporate Offices, 1301 Atwood Ave., P.O. Box 7500, Johnston, RI 02919

Web site: www.fmglobal.com

International Fire Marshal's Association (formerly Fire Marshal's Association of American Bar Association)

Association of municipal, county, state, provincial fire marshals, and fire prevention bureau officials. Affiliated with the National Fire Protection Association. The Fire Marshal's Association promotes arson control and fire prevention through the exchange of information between its members.

Address: Steven F. Sawyer, IFMA Executive Secretary, 1 Batterymarch Park, Quincy, MA 02619-7471

Telephone: 617-784-7424

e-mail: IFMA@nfpa.org
Web site: www.nfpa.org

International Code Council (ICC)

Established in 1994 as a nonprofit organization, the ICC has developed a single set of comprehensive and coordinated national model construction codes. Prior to establishing the ICC, its founders (the Building Officials and Code Administrators International, Inc. [BOCA], International Conference of Building Officials [ICBO], and Southern Building Code Congress International, Inc. [SBCCI]) developed the three separate sets of model codes used throughout the United States. The offices of the founding agencies now serve as regional offices for the ICC.

Address: 5203 Leesburg Pike, Suite 600, Falls Church, VA 22041

Web site: www.intlcode.org

International Code Council

Many jurisdictions still use codes adopted from the model codes created by BOCA, ICBO, and SBCCI. For this reason, the editors feel it is important to provide some historical information regarding these agencies.

Building Officials And Code Administrators International Inc. (BOCA)

BOCA is an organization that provides model codes for city and state adoption. The model codes are for building, mechanical, plumbing, and fire prevention. BOCA also sponsors training, testing, and certification for code administrators and building inspection officials. At the time this manual was written, BOCA was in the process of consolidating its offices and operations under the ICC organization.

Address: 4051 W. Flossmoore Rd., Country Club Hills, IL 60477

Web site: www.bocai.org

International Conference of Building Officials (ICBO)

ICBO is an organization that provides the Uniform Building Code (UBC) for city and state adoption. The UBC is found mostly in western states and some southern cities. ICBO produces fire codes in conjunction with the Western Fire Chiefs Association. ICBO also sponsors training, testing, and certification for code administrators and building inspection officials. At the time this manual was written, ICBO was in the process of consolidating its offices and operations under the ICC organization.

Address: 5360 South Workman Mill Road, Whittier, CA 90601-2298

Web site: www.icbo.org

Southern Building Code Congress International (SBCCI)

SBCCI is an organization that provides the Standard Building Code for city and state adoption. The SBCCI also has mechanical, plumbing, and fire prevention codes. The SBCCI is found mostly in the southern states. SBCCI also sponsors training, testing, and certification for code administrators and building inspection officials. At the time this manual was written, SBCCI was in the process of consolidating its offices and operations under the ICC organization.

Address: 900 Montclair Road, Birmingham, AL 35213-1206

Web site: www.sbcci.org

Insurance Information Institute

Property and casualty insurance companies. Seeks to improve public understanding. Founded in 1960.

Address: 110 William Street, 24th Floor, New York, NY 10038

Telephone: 212-346-5500

Web site: www.iii.org

International Association of Arson Investigators (IAAI)

Individuals may join the IAAI as active members if they are currently engaged in suppressing arson for a government or private organization. Others may join as associate members if they meet IAAI requirements. The primary function of the association is attacking the problem of arson.

Address: 12770 Boenker Road, Bridgeton, MO 63044

Telephone: 314-739-4224

Web site: www.firearson.com

International Association of Chiefs of Police

Association of police executives. Provides consultation and research services in all phases of police activity. Founded in 1893.

Address: 515 N. Washington St., Alexandria, VA 22314

Telephone: 703-836-6767 or 1-800-THE-IACP

Web site: www.theiacp.org

International Association of Fire Chiefs

Fire chiefs in city and state departments, industrial and military installations; equipment manufacturers, and others interested in fire prevention and protection. Founded in 1873.

Address: 4025 Fair Ridge Dr., Suite 300, Fairfax, VA 22033-2868

Telephone: 703-273-0911

Web site: www.iafc.org

National Association of Fire Investigators (NAFI)

Non-profit organization dedicated to helping increase the knowledge and skills of persons engaged in the investigation of fires, explosions, arson, subrogation, fire prevention, and related fields, or in the litigation which ensues from such investigation. Incorporated in 1961.

Address: 857 Tallevast Rd, Sarasota, FL 34243

Telephone: 1-877-506-NAFI (US and Canada)

Web site: www.nafi.org

National Association of Insurance Commissioners

State officials supervising insurance. Promotes uniformity of legislation and regulations affecting insurance to protect interests of policyholders. Founded in 1871.

Address (Executive Headquarters): 2301 McGee Street, Suite 800, Kansas City, MO 64108-2662

Telephone: 816-842-3600

Web site: www.naic.org

National Association of Mutual Insurance Companies

Mutual fire and casualty insurance companies. Gathers, compiles, and analyzes information on all matters relating to insurance and to the reduction and prevention of losses. Founded in 1895.

Address: 3601 Vincennes Rd., Indianapolis, IN 46268-0700

Telephone: 317-875-5250

Web site: www.namic.org

National Association of State Fire Marshals (NASFM)

Represents the most senior fire official of each of the 50 United States and District of Columbia. Goal is to improve efficiency and effectiveness of state fire marshals' operations, which include fire safety code adoption and enforcement, fire and arson investigation, fire incident data reporting and analysis, public education and advising Governors and State Legislatures on fire protection. Most members appointed by Governors or other high-ranking state officials.

Address NASFM Administration Office: P.O. Box 4137, Clifton Park, NY 12065

Telephone: 877-996-2736

Web site: www.firemarshals.org

National Crime Prevention Council

National nonprofit educational organization designed to address all sources of major crime in the United States and to serve as a source of help for individuals, neighborhoods, communities, and governments. The organizational meeting was held in Chicago in 1976.

Address: 1000 Connecticut Avenue, NW, 13th Floor, Washington, DC 20036

Telephone: 202-466-6272

Web site: www.ncpc.org

National District Attorneys Association

Prosecuting attorneys and assistant prosecuting attorneys who are associated members. Carries out educational and information programs to keep prosecuting attorneys informed in the field of criminal justice and individual civil liberties. Founded in 1950.

Address: 99 Canal Center Plaza, Suite 510, Alexandria, VA 22314

Telephone: 703-549-9222

Web site: www.ndaa.org

National Fire Academy

An element of the Federal Emergency Management Agency which was established to advance the professional development of fire service personnel and other persons engaged in fire prevention and control activities. The Academy provides programs at the resident facility and in the field through state and local fire training agencies.

Address: 16825 S. Seton Ave., Emmitsburg, MD 21727

Telephone: 301-447-1176

Web site:
www.usfa.fema.gov/fire-service/nfa/nfa.shtm

National Institute of Standards and Technology (NIST)

Founded in 1901, NIST is a non-regulatory federal agency within the U.S. Commerce Department's Technology Administration. Its mission is to perform and support research on all aspects of fire and to provide scientific and technical knowledge applicable to the prevention and control of fires.

Establishes its content and priorities of the research program in consultation with the U.S. Fire Administration. Results of its research will be encouraged to be incorporated in building codes, fire codes, fire service operations, training, and standards.

Address: 100 Bureau Drive, Gaithersburg, MD 20899-3460

Telephone Public Inquiries Unit:
301- 975-NIST (6478)

Web site: www.nist.gov

National Fire Protection Association

Comprehensive national organization including representatives of business and industry, public safety officials, fire insurance executives and engineers, colleges, hospitals, libraries, and the general public. Serves as clearinghouse for fire information. Through some 159 technical committees, develops and publishes advisory standards on practically every aspect of fire protection and prevention. Founded in 1896.

Address: 1 Batterymarch Park, Quincy, MA 02619-7471

Telephone: 617-770-3300

Web site: www.nfpa.org

Technical Standards & Safety Authority (Canada)

An independent, not-for-profit organization responsible for the delivery of various safety programs and services including the administration of Ontario's *Technical Standards & Safety Act, 2000.* Develop develops training standards, reviews regulations, and provides input to help shape the procedures related to the certification of industry trades and occupations. It is also instrumental in developing and implementing new certification programs. They offer a number of safety-related programs and training courses, including a series of testing and safety programs.

Address: Technical Standards & Safety Authority 14th Floor, Centre Tower, 3300 Bloor Street West Toronto, Ontario Canada M8X 2X4

Telephone: 416-734-3300

Web site: www.tssa.org

Underwriters Laboratories Inc. (UL)

The goal of UL is to promote public safety through its scientific investigation of various materials to determine how hazardous the materials are. After testing, the organization then lists and marks the material as having passed its rigorous tests. The nonprofit UL was founded in 1894.

Address: 333 Pfingsten Road, Northbrook, IL 60062-2096

Web site: www.ul.com

Underwriters Laboratories of Canada (ULC)

An affiliate of the Underwriters Laboratory, ULC's goal is to promote public safety through its scientific investigation of various materials to determine how hazardous the materials are. After testing, the organization then lists and marks the material as having passed its rigorous tests. The nonprofit UL was founded in 1920.

Address: 7 Underwriters Road, Toronto, ON, M1R 3B4

Web site: www.ulc.ca

U.S. Fire Administration

An agency of the Federal Emergency Management Agency was established to reduce the nation's human, property, and economic losses from fire by better fire prevention and control efforts.

Address: 16825 South Seton Avenue, Emmitsburg, MD 21727

Web site: www.usfa.fema.gov

U.S. Forest Service

The Forest Service was established in 1905 and is an agency of the U.S. Department of Agriculture. The Forest Service manages public lands in national forests and grasslands, which encompass 191 million acres. The Forest Service provides technical and financial assistance to state and private forest landowners as well as to cities and communities to improve the natural environment. Develops and provides scientific and technical knowledge aimed at improving the capability to protect, manage, and use forests and rangelands. Maintains public records concerning forestry and mining activities.

Address: USDA Forest Service, 1400 Independence Ave., SW, Washington, D.C. 20250-0003

Web site: www.fs.fed.us

Appendix B
Federal Constitutional Search and Seizure Issues in Fire Scene Investigations[1]

Introduction

This memorandum summarizes the state of the law with respect to federal constitutional search and seizure issues in fire scene investigations. It does not address search and seizure issues with respect to State law, which might afford more protection to property owners and place greater restraint on fire investigators than does the federal constitution. See *Mills v. Rogers*, 457 U.S. 291, 303 (1982). However, because the federal constitution provides the minimum level of search and seizure protection below which the States may not stray, this summarization provides the minimum level of protection generally applicable in the United States. Id.

The Law

The Supreme Court outlined the Fourth Amendment search and seizure protections applicable to fire scene investigations in the cases of *Michigan v. Tyler*, 436 U.S. 499 (1978), and *Michigan v. Clifford*, 464 U.S. 287 (1984). In these cases, the Court held that the conduct of fire scene investigations fall within the strictures of the Fourth Amendment's protection against unreasonable searches and seizures. *Tyler*, 436 U.S. 499, 506 (1978). Accordingly, the general rule is that fire investigators may not make a nonconsensual entry onto private property without a duly authorized search warrant. *Tyler*, 436 U.S. at 506. However, the Court granted fire investigators some latitude to conduct warrantless searches of fire scenes by allowing fire officials to remain on private property for a reasonable time after the fire has been extinguished, and by allowing the use of administrative search warrants for routine fire investigations.

The Court has recognized that "[a] burning building clearly presents an exigency of sufficient proportions to render a warrantless entry 'reasonable.'" Id. at 509. Because the firefighting function encompasses "not only ... extinguishing fires, but with finding their causes," fire officials can remain on private property for a "reasonable time" after the fire has been extinguished to determine the origin of the blaze. Id. at 510. However, what constitutes a "reasonable" time is a very fact specific determination that may vary with the circumstances of each case. Id. at 510 n. 6.

In order to obtain a search warrant for the purpose of conducting a routine investigation into the origin of an unexplained fire, fire officials need only establish the level of probable cause required for administrative searches. *Michigan v. Clifford*, 464 U.S. 287, 294 (1984). This level of probable cause is established upon a showing that "reasonable legislative or administrative standards for conducting an ... inspection are satisfied with respect to a particular dwelling." *Camara v. Municipal* Court, 387 U.S. 523, 538. As applied in the fire investigation context, this standard requires fire investigators to "show only that a fire of undetermined origin has occurred on the premises, that the scope of the proposed search is reasonable and will not intrude unnecessarily on the fire victim's privacy, and that the search will be executed at a reasonable and convenient time." *Michigan v. Clifford*, 464 U.S. 287, 294 (1984). However, to search for evidence of arson, officials must establish the traditional level of probable cause required of searches for evidence of crime. *Tyler*, 436 U.S. at 512. Criminal search warrants require a showing that the facts and circumstances of which investigators have "reasonably trustworthy information" are sufficient to cause a person of "reasonable caution" to believe that an offense has been committed. *Draper v. United States*, 358 U.S. 307, 313 (1959).

Supreme Court Cases

Michigan v. Tyler, 436 U.S. 499 (1978)

In *Tyler*, a fire department responding to a midnight fire in a furniture store was able to control the blaze by approximately 2:00 a.m. As the firefighters were "watering down smoldering embers," the Fire Chief arrived and entered the smoking building to examine two containers of flammable liquid that had been found in the store. Believing the fire "could possibly have been arson," the Fire Chief called a detective who arrived at approximately 3:30 a.m. *Tyler* at 502. The detective entered the building to begin his investigation, but was forced to abandon the effort because of steam and smoke in the building. The firefighters completely extinguished the fire and departed by 4:00 a.m. At approximately 8:00 a.m., the Chief returned with the Assistant Chief for a brief examination of the scene. The Assistant Chief returned again at 9:00 a.m. with the detective. They found and seized evidence of arson, including what appeared to be a fuse trail burned into the carpet. Several weeks later, other investigators returned to the scene and found further evidence of arson. Although the building owners did not object to theses entries and seizures at the time, they objected when the evidence was introduced against them at trial. The Michigan Supreme Court held that all the entries made by fire investigators after the flames had been extinguished were illegal warrantless searches, ruled inadmissible any evidence found as a result of these entries, and reversed the convictions of the defendants.

The U.S. Supreme Court held that a property owner's reasonable expectation of privacy is not destroyed simply because his property has been damaged by fire. *Tyler*, 436 U.S. at 505. Having established that an expectation of privacy remained, the property owner was protected by the Fourth Amendment's prohibition on unreasonable searches and seizures. Id. at 506. However, the Court also recognized that there are circumstances in which official action is compelled, but there is no time to obtain a search warrant. Such compel-ling circumstances can arise in either a criminal investigation or administrative inspection context. Id. at 509.

The Court held that a "burning building clearly presents an exigency of sufficient proportions to render a warrantless entry [to put out the blaze] 'reasonable.' ... [O]nce in the building for this purpose, firefighters may seize evidence of arson that is in plain view." Id. at 509. In addition, because "[fire officials are charged not only with extinguishing fires, but with finding their causes ... [they] need no warrant to remain in a building for a reasonable time to investigate the cause of a blaze after it has been extinguished." Id. at 510. What constitutes "a reasonable time" is a very fact specific determination. The Court commented in a footnote that a number of factors go into the "reasonableness" determination, including the type of structure, the size of the fire, as well as the individual's reasonable expectation of privacy. Id. at 510 n. 6. In this case, the Court decided that the warrantless re-entries of the property the following morning were justified as "no more than an actual continuation of the first [entry], and the lack of a warrant did not invalidate the resulting seizure of evidence." Id. at 511. However, the entries onto the property weeks later were found to be "clearly detached from the initial exigency." Id. at 511. Because investigators obtained neither administrative nor criminal search warrants for these later entries, the evidence obtained was inadmissible at trial. Id. at 511.

Michigan v. Clifford, 464 U.S. 287 (1984)

After an early morning fire at the Cliffords' residence was extinguished at 7:04 a.m., all police and firefighters left the scene. Arson investigators, having been notified that the fire was suspicious, arrived at the scene five hours later. They found a work crew busy, on the vacationing Cliffords' instructions, securing the house and pumping water from the basement. While waiting for the water to be pumped, the investigators found a fuel can in the driveway that had been removed by firefighters and seized it as evidence. Although the investigators knew that the Cliffords had given instructions to secure the house, they entered the residence without consent or a warrant and conducted a thorough search. In the basement they found two more fuel cans and a crock pot attached to a timer, which they also seized as evidence. They then continued their search into the living areas of the residence and found further evidence of arson. Before trial, the Cliffords moved to exclude all evidence that was seized during this search of their residence.

The Supreme Court rejected the State's assertion that all postfire administrative searches should be exempt from warrant requirements, and affirmed the principle that, absent exceptional circumstances, all nonconsensual searches require warrants. *Clifford*, 464 U.S. at 291-92. The Court also rejected the State's suggestion that the *Tyler* principle allowed the warrantless postfire search as a continuation of the entry made by the firefighters. The Court distinguished the two cases not on legal principle, but on the particular facts of each case.

In *Tyler*, investigators were forced to call off the initial attempt at investigation because of smoke and darkness, but resumed the search as soon as practicable. *Tyler*, at 296. The Court found that the Cliffords' efforts to secure their residence during the time between the departure of the firefighters and the arrival of the arson investigators separated the entry of the firefighters and the entry of the investigators into two different events and precluded considering the investigators' entry a continuation of the firefighters valid entry.

The Court also found that the Cliffords' privacy interest in their residence, particularly because they had taken steps to secure it, was greater than the owner's interest in the furniture store in *Tyler*. The Court held that "[a]t least where a homeowner has made a reasonable effort to secure his fire damaged home ... we hold that a subsequent postfire search must be conducted pursuant to a warrant, consent, or the identification of some new exigency. So long as the primary purpose is to ascertain the cause of the fire, an administrative warrant will suffice." *Clifford*, at 297. Because no warrant was obtained before the investigators entered the Clifford home, all evidence found during their entry was inadmissible as evidence. Id. at 287.

While not stating it explicitly, the Court implied that even though the investigators were suspicious of arson, an administrative warrant would have sufficed for the initial basement search. The Court noted that even if the investigator's initial search

of the basement had been pursuant to a duly authorized administrative search warrant, continuation of the search into the living quarters of the residence was not authorized. Id. at 287. However, because the purpose of an administrative search is to determine the origin of the fire and preclude its rekindling, "not [to] give fire officials license to roam freely throughout the fire victim's private residence," once investigators had determined the cause of the fire was the crock pot and timer they would have exhausted their search authority. Id. at 297-98.

Nevertheless, the one fuel can seized from the driveway by investigators was admissible as evidence. Id. at 299. Because this can was seen in plain view when the investigators arrived at the scene and had been in plain view when the firefighters had entered the house to extinguish the blaze, it was admissible whether it had been seized by the firefighters or the investigators. Id.

[1]By David M. Bessho, Georgia State University, College of Law, Atlanta, Georgia.

Prepared for Michael A. McKenzie; Cozen and O'Connor; Suite 200; One Peachtree Street, NE; Atlanta, Georgia 30308.

Appendix C
Collecting And Preserving Physical Evidence*

Specimen	Identification	Amount Desired		Preservation Methods	Special Packaging
		Sample	Evidence		
Abrasives, including Carborundum, sand, and the like	Mark the outside of container with the type of material enclosed, the date obtained, and the collector's name or number. If possible, include the case number and sample number.	Not less than 1 ounce	All	None	Use container such as pill box, powder box, or paper bindle. Seal to prevent loss.
Acids	Same as above. Mark "Corrosive"	1 pint	All to 1 pint	Do not send through the mail. Use extreme caution in handling.	Use glass bottle. Tape in stopper. (Exception: If Hydrochloric acid, contact laboratory.)
Adhesive tape	Same as above	1 foot or all. Make sure to send end piece	All	Use caution regarding fingerprints	Suspend between supports or place on waxed paper or cellophane. DO NOT BALL UP.
Alkalies — caustics, soda, potash, ammonia and the like	Same as above. Mark "Corrosive"	1 pint liquid 1 pound solid	All to 1 pint All to 1 pound	Do not send through the mail. Use extreme caution in handling.	Use glass bottle with rubber stopper; hold in with adhesive tape.
Ammunition	Same as above.	6	All	Do not send through the mail.	Pack in tissue, soft paper, or cloth in small box.
Anonymous letters, extortion letters	Place in paper envelope; seal with evidence sticker. Place date and officer's mark on sticker.		All	Do not handle with bare hands. Do not fold.	Wrap securely. Place envelope in manila envelope.
Fire debris	Label as to origin, sample number, and name of collector. Note if there is an odor present or a reading on hydrocarbon sniffer.	1 quart of suspect debris	Fill can nearly to top. Leave air space.	Do not send petroleum products throught the mail.	Seal in clean, metal can, or glass jar.
Blasting cap	Call Laboratory			Do not bring to laboratory or send through mail.	

Specimen	Identification	Amount Desired		Preservation Methods	Special Packaging
		Sample	Evidence		
Bullets (not cartridges)	Do not mark bullet. Place bullet in container.	All	All	None	Place in soft tissue, per instructions, seal, box or match box. Label container.
Cartridge cases	Same as bullets	All	All	None	Same as above.
Charred or burned paper.	On outside of container Indicate type of material, date obtained, collector's name and number.		All	Pack loosely on soft cotton.	Pack in rigid Container. Label "Fragile."
Checks (fraudulent)	See anonymous letters.		All	None	Package
Check protector	Place collector's mark on sample impressions.	Obtain several copies in full word-For-word order of each questioned check-writer impression.		None	Tag and place properly.
Clothing	Mark officer's Initials and badge number Directly on clothing in the waistband, pocket, or collar.	Where dust in cuffs is of interest, roll them up a couple of folds before rolling up the rest of the trousers so loss will be minimized. Take care not to transfer materials or to contaminate other clothing	All	If clothing is wet with blood, hang to air dry before packaging to prevent putrefaction; do not ball up; fold neatly with clean paper between folds and refrigerate if possible.	Individually wrap each article and place in paper bag. Write identification on the outside of package. Place in strong container.
Drugs a. Liquids b. Powder, polls, and solids	Mark bottles and label.	All	All	None	Seal in evidence Envelope.
Explosives		Call laboratory.			
Glass fragments	Mark on outside of container the type of material, date, and officer's name and number.	1-inch square from each source.	All	Keep evidence separated from sample.	Use pill box, paper bindle, or cellophane bag. Pack and seal to avoid movement in container.

Specimen	Identification	Amount Desired		Preservation Methods	Special Packaging
		Sample	**Evidence**		
Firearms	place serial number in officer's notes. Also note the make of weapon and barrel length (some manufacturers of inexpensive weapons duplicate serial numbers on guns of different barrel lengths.)	All		Unload. Note cylinder position. If automatic, do not handle side of clip because possible fingerprints may be in this location.	Place revolvers and automatics in manila envelopes. Tag rifles.
Hairs and fibers	Label outside of container with the type of material, date, and officer's name and number.	Several hairs. All should have representative specimen from all parts of head and body.	All	Call laboratory for specific recommendations.	Use pill box, paper bindle, or cellophane bag. Seal.
Metal	Same as above.	1 pound	All to 1 pound	Keep from rusting.	Place in large envelope if possible.
Oil	Same as above.	1 quart with specifications	All to 1 quart	None	Seal in sealed bottle or metal screw-top can. Sample all layers of oil if contaminated with unknown substance.
Paint: a. Liquid	Mark the outside of container with the type of material enclosed, origin if known, date, and officer's name and number.	1/4 pint	All to 1/4 pint	None	Metal can or glass jar. Seal.
b. Solid		At least 1/2 square Inch of solid	All; if on small object, end object.	Caution to obtain sample from transfer area.	Pill box, paper bindle, or cellophane Bag. Seal.
Rope, twine, and cordage	Label the tag or container with the type of material enclosed, the date, and officer's name and number.	1 yard	All	None	Place in envelope or wrap in paper. Seal.
Safe insulation or soil	Label the outside of container with type of material enclosed, origin if known, date, and officer's name and number.	1/2 pound	All to 1 pound	None	Place in box. Seal to prevent loss.

Specimen	Identification	Amount Desired		Preservation Methods	Special Packaging
		Sample	Evidence		
Tools	Label tool with officer's mark.	All	All	Place envelope or folded sheet of paper carefully over end of tool to prevent damage and loss of adhering paints, and the like.	Wrap each tool separately to prevent shifting.
Tool Marks	Mark object or tag attached to it. Mark on opposite end from tool marks. Include the officer's mark and date.	Send in tool if found.	All marks	Cover marks with soft paper and wrap with strong paper.	After marks have been protected, wrap in strong wrapping paper, and place in envelope.
Wire	Mark label or tag. Include the type of material, date, and officer's name and serial number.	1 foot	All	If for cutter tool mark comparisons, DISTINCTLY MARK, twist, or otherwise label the end representing the cut-off end.	Wrap securely.
Wood	Place officer's mark directly on wood; also label as above.	1 foot	All		Wrap securely.
Wood shavings and borings from auger	Place in box. Label as above.	1 foot	All	Pack loosely to avoid breaking chips and shavings.	Place in loose bag or box. Seal to prevent loss.

*This chart is not intended to be all-inclusive. If evidence to be preserved is not found herein, an investigator should consult the specimen list for an item most similar in nature and submit accordingly. If any instance where an investigator is in doubt as to the appropriate procedure, he/she should consult a criminalist at the receiving lab or defer to crime laboratory personnel assigned to fire scene investigation.

Glossary/Index

Glossary

A

Absorption — (1) The penetration of one substance into the structure of another such as the process of picking up a liquid contaminant with an absorbent. (2) Passage of materials (such as toxins) through some body surface into body fluids and tissue.

Accelerant — Material, usually a flammable or combustible liquid, that is used to initiate or increase the spread of a fire.

Accessory — Someone who aids in the commission of a crime.

Accident — Sequence of unplanned or uncontrolled events that produces unintended injury, death, or property damage; the result of unsafe acts by persons who are unaware or uninformed of potential hazards and ignorant of safety policies or who fail to follow safety procedures.

Adjoining — Sharing a common boundary.

Adjudicate — To hear and settle a case by judicial procedure.

Administrative Law — Body of law created by an administrative agency in the form of rules, regulations, orders, and decisions to carry out regulatory powers and duties of the agency.

Aerosol — A suspension of liquid or solid particles in air or gas.

Agency — (1) An administrative unit of government. (2) A legal relationship in which one person (the agent) can act on behalf of another (the principal).

Alpha Radiation — Consists of particles having a large mass and a positive electrical charge; least penetrating of the three common forms of radioactive substances. It is normally not considered dangerous to plants, animals, or people unless it gets into the body.

Ambient Temperature — Temperature of the surrounding environment.

Arc — A luminous discharge of electricity across a gap. Arcs produce very high temperature.

Area of Origin — Location (room or area) where a fire originated.

Arson — Crime of willfully, maliciously, and intentionally starting a fire (firesetting) or causing an explosion to destroy one's property or the property of another. Precise legal definitions vary among jurisdictions, wherein it is defined by statutes and judicial decisions.

Attack — (1) To set upon forcefully. (2) Any action to control fire. (3) In ICS/IMS, used to describe the units attacking the fire.

Authority Having Jurisdiction — Term used in codes and standards to identify the legal entity, such as a building or fire official, that has the statutory authority to enforce a code and to approve or require equipment. In the insurance industry it may refer to an insurance rating bureau or an insurance company inspection department.

Autoignition — Ignition that occurs when a substance in air, whether solid, liquid, or gaseous, is heated sufficiently to initiate or cause self-sustained combustion without an external ignition source.

B

Backdraft — (1) Instantaneous explosion or rapid burning of superheated gases that occurs when oxygen is introduced into an oxygen-depleted confined space. The stalled combustion resumes with explosive force. It may occur because of inadequate or improper ventilation procedures. (2) Very rapid, often explosive burning of hot gases that occurs when oxygen is introduced into an oxygen-depleted confined space. It may occur because of inadequate or improper ventilation procedures.

Bearing Wall — Wall that supports itself and the weight of the roof and/or other internal structural framing components such as the floor beams above it.

Beta Radiation — Type of radiation that can cause skin burns.

Bill of Lading—Shipping paper used by the trucking industry indicating origin, destination, route, and product. There is a bill of lading in the cab of every truck tractor. This document establishes the terms of a contract between a shipper and a transportation company. It serves as a document of title, a contract of carriage, and a receipt for goods.

Blacken—To "knock down" a fire; to reduce a fire by extinguishing all visible flame. As the flame is extinguished, the fire is said to be blackened.

Blast Area—Area affected by the blast wave from an explosion.

Bloodborne Pathogens—Pathogenic microorganisms that are present in the human blood and can cause disease in humans. These pathogens include (but are not limited to) hepatitis B virus (HBV) and human immunodeficiency virus (HIV).

Boiling Liquid Expanding Vapor Explosion (BLEVE) — Rapid vaporization of a liquid stored under pressure upon release to the atmosphere following major failure of its containing vessel. The failure of the containing vessel is the result of over-pressurization caused by an external heat source causing the vessel to explode into two or more pieces when the temperature of the liquid is well above its boiling point at normal atmospheric pressure.

Boiling Point—Temperature of a substance when the vapor pressure exceeds atmospheric pressure. At this temperature, the rate of evaporation exceeds the rate of condensation. At this point, more liquid is turning into gas than gas is turning back into a liquid.

Bomb Squad — Crew of emergency responders specially trained and equipped to deal with explosive devices.

Bonding — (1) Connection of two objects with a metal chain or strap in order to neutralize the static electrical charge between the two. (2) Gluing two objects together.

Branch Circuit — The wiring between the point of application (outlets) and the final overcurrent device protecting the circuit.

Brands — Large, burning embers that are lifted by a fire's thermal column and carried away with the wind.

Brick-Joisted — Brick or masonry wall structure with wooden floors and roof. Commonly known as ordinary construction.

British Thermal Unit (Btu) — Amount of heat energy required to raise the temperature of one pound of water one degree Fahrenheit. One Btu = 1.055 kilo joules (kJ).

Building Code — Body of local law, adopted by states, counties, cities, or other governmental bodies to regulate the construction, renovation, and maintenance of buildings.

Building Engineer — Person who is familiar with and responsible for the operation of a building's heating, ventilating, and air-conditioning (HVAC) system and other essential equipment.

Bureau of Alcohol, Tobacco, and Firearms (ATF) — Division of the U.S. Department of Treasury that regulates the storage, handling, and transportation of explosives.

Burn Pattern — Apparent and obvious design of burned material and the burning path of travel from a point of fire origin.

C

Calorie — Amount of heat needed to raise the temperature of one gram of water one degree Centigrade.

Canadian Standards Association (CSA) — Canadian standards-writing organization.

Carbonaceous Material — Material that contains carbon.

Carbon Dioxide (CO_2)—Colorless, odorless, heavier than air gas that neither supports combustion nor burns. CO_2 is used in portable fire extinguishers as an extinguishing agent to extinguish Class B or C fires by smothering or displacing the oxygen. CO_2 is a waste product of aerobic metabolism.

Carbon Dioxide System — Extinguishing system that uses carbon dioxide as the primary extinguishing agent; designed primarily to protect confined spaces because the gaseous agent is easily dispersed by wind.

Carbon Monoxide (CO) — Colorless, odorless, dangerous gas (both toxic and flammable) formed by the incomplete combustion of carbon. It combines more than 200 times more quickly with hemoglobin than oxygen thus decreasing the blood's ability to carry oxygen.

Carcinogen — Cancer-producing substance.

Cargo Manifest — Document or shipping paper listing all contents carried by a vehicle or vessel on a specific trip.

Case Law — Laws based on judicial interpretations and decisions rather than created by legislation.

Catalyst — Substance that modifies (usually increases) the rate of a chemical reaction without being consumed in the process.

Centigrade (Celsius) — Temperature scale in which the boiling point of water is 100°C (212°F) and the freezing point is 0°C (32°F) at normal atmospheric pressure.

Certificate of Occupancy — Issued by a building official after all required electrical, gas, mechanical, plumbing, and fire protection systems have been inspected for compliance with the technical codes and other applicable laws and ordinances.

Certification — (1) A certified statement. (2) Refers to a manufacturer's certification; for example that a ladder has been constructed to meet requirements of NFPA 1931. (3) Issuance of a document that states one has demonstrated the knowledge and skills necessary to function in a field.

CFR — (1) Abbreviation for *Code of Federal Regulations*. (2) Abbreviation for Crash Fire Rescue.

Chain of Command — (1) Order of rank and authority in the fire service. (2) The proper sequence of information and command flow as described in the incident command system.

Chain of Custody — Continuous changes of possession of physical "evidence" that must be established in court to admit such material into evidence.

Chain Reaction — Series of self-sustaining changes each of which causes or influences a similar reaction.

Char — Carbonaceous material formed by incomplete combustion of an organic material, commonly wood; the remains of burned materials.

Charged Building — Building heavily laden with heat, smoke, and gases, and possibly in danger of having a backdraft.

Chemical Chain Reaction — One of the four sides of the fire tetrahedron representing a process occurring during a fire: Vapor or gases are distilled from flammable materials during initial burning. Atoms and molecules are released from these vapors and combine with other radicals to form new compounds. These compounds are again disturbed by the heat, releasing more atoms and radicals that form new compounds. Interrupting the chain reaction stops the overall reaction and is the extinguishing mechanism utilized by several extinguishing agents.

Chemical Entry Suit — Protective apparel designed to protect the firefighter's body from certain liquid or gaseous chemicals. May be used to describe both Level A and Level B protection.

Chemical Flame Inhibition — The extinguishment of a fire by interruption of the chemical chain reaction.

Chemical Heat Energy — Heat produced from a chemical reaction including combustion, spontaneous heating, heat of decomposition, and heat of solution; sometimes occurs as a result of a material being improperly used or stored. Some materials may simply come in contact with each other and react, or they may decompose and generate heat.

Chief Officer — Any of the higher officer grades, from district or battalion chief to the chief of the fire department.

Chimney Effect — Created when a ventilation opening is made in the upper portion of a building and air currents throughout the building are drawn in the direction of the opening; also occurs in wildland fires when the fire advances up a V-shaped drainage swale.

Circuit — Complete path of an electrical current.

Circuit Breaker — Device (basically an on/off switch) designed to allow a circuit to be opened or closed manually, and to automatically interrupt the flow of electricity in a circuit when it becomes overloaded.

Circumstantial Evidence — Facts from which presumptions or inferences are made; indirect evidence. For example, seeing a person flee from the scene of an arson is circumstantial or indirect evidence that the person committed the crime. Seeing the person set the fire is direct evidence.

Citation — Notice of a violation of law.

Civil Liability — Legal responsibility for fulfilling a specified duty or behaving with due regard for the rights and safety of others.

Class A Fire — Fire involving ordinary combustibles such as wood, paper, cloth, and similar materials.

Class B Fire — Fires of flammable and combustible liquids and gases such as gasoline, kerosene, and propane.

Class C Fire — Fires involving energized electrical equipment.

Class D Fire — Fires of combustible metals such as magnesium, sodium, and titanium.

Class K Fire — Fires in cooking appliances that involve combustible cooking media (vegetable or animal oils and fats). Commonly occurs in commercial cooking facilities such as restaurants and institutional kitchens.

CNG — Abbreviation for Compressed Natural Gas.

CO — Chemical formula and abbreviation for carbon monoxide.

CO_2 — Chemical formula and abbreviation for carbon dioxide.

Code — A body of laws arranged systematically usually pertaining to one subject area such as a mechanical code, a building code, an electrical code, or a fire code.

Code for Safety to Life from Fire in Buildings and Structures — Old title of NFPA 101, Life Safety Code®.

Code of Federal Regulations (CFR) — Formal name given to the books or documents containing the specific United States regulations provided for by law. The complete body of U.S. Federal law.

Coercion — The act of forcing or compelling (by use of threats, authority, or any other means) someone to perform an act, make a choice or to comply.

Combustible Gas Detector — Device that indicates the explosive levels of combustible gases.

Combustible Liquid — Liquid having a flash point at or above 100°F (37.8°C) and below 200°F (93.3°C).

Combustion — An exothermic chemical reaction that is a self-sustaining process of rapid oxidation of a fuel, that produces heat and light.

Combustion — An exothermic chemical reaction that is a self-sustaining process of rapid oxidation of a fuel that produces heat and light.

Command — (1) Act of directing, ordering, and/or controlling resources by virtue of explicit legal, agency, or delegated authority. (2) Term used on the radio to designate the incident commander. (3) Function of IMS that determines the overall strategy of the incident, with input from throughout the IMS structure.

Command Post (CP) — The designated physical location of the command and control point where the incident commander and command staff function during an incident and where those in charge of emergency units report to be briefed on their respective assignments.

Commissioner — Member of city or county government. The fire commissioner represents the fire department on the government ruling body. In some cases, there is no commissioner and the fire chief is the ranking official directly responsible to the government.

Common Hazard — Condition likely to be found in almost all occupancies and generally not associated with a specific occupancy or activity.

Common Law — Law not created by legislative action but based on certain commonly held customs, traditions, and beliefs within a particular culture.

Compartment Fire — Fire that occurs within a room or space that influences the development of the fire.

Competent Ignition Source — Any heat energy source that can transfer sufficient heat energy to a fuel to establish flaming combustion.

Compliance — Meeting the minimum standards set forth by applicable codes or regulations.

Compressed Gas — Gas that at normal temperature exists solely as a gas when pressurized in a container as opposed to a gas that becomes a liquid when stored under pressure.

Concealed Space — Any structural void that is not readily visible from a living/working space within a building such as areas between walls or partitions, ceilings and roofs, and floors and basement ceilings through which fire may spread undetected; also includes soffits and other enclosed vertical or horizontal shafts through which fire may spread.

Condensation — Process of going from the gaseous to the liquid state.

Conduction — Physical flow or transfer of heat energy from one body to another through direct contact or an intervening medium from the point where the heat is produced to another location or from a region of high temperature to a region of low temperature.

Conductivity — The ability of a substance to conduct an electrical current.

Confined Space — Any space or enclosed area not intended for continuous occupation, having limited (restricted access) openings for entry or exit, providing unfavorable natural ventilation and the potential to have a toxic, explosive, or oxygen-deficient atmosphere.

Consensus Standard — Rules, principles, or measures that are established though agreement of members of the standards-setting organization.

Consumer Product Safety Commission (CPSC) — U.S. federal agency that operates the National Electronic Injury Surveillance System (NEISS) database since 1972. Data is based on a sample of hospital emergency rooms, focusing on the role of consumer products in fire and burn injuries.

Contributory Negligence — Carelessness of the injured person that helped to cause the accident in which he was injured.

Convection — Transfer of heat by the movement of heated fluids or gases, usually in an upward direction.

Convection Column — Rising column of heated air or gases above a continuing heat or fire source. Also known as Thermal Column.

Convenience Outlet — Electrical outlet that can be used for lamps and other appliances.

County/Parish — Political subdivision of a state, province, or territory for administrative purposes and public safety.

Criminal Law — Law intended to protect society by identifying certain conduct as criminal and by specifying the sanctions to be imposed on those who engage in criminal activity.

Criminal Negligence — An act of negligence that is a violation of law and constitutes a crime.

Crowd Control — Limiting access to an emergency scene by curious spectators and other non-emergency personnel.

CSA — Abbreviation for Canadian Standards Association.

Culpable Negligence — Either acting or failing to act in a reasonably cautious manner with the result that another person is placed at risk of injury or death.

Current — The rate of electrical flow in a conductor, measured in amperes.

D

Damage — Loss, injury, or deterioration caused by the negligence, design, or accident of one person to another in respect to another person's property.

Damages — Compensation to a person for any loss, detriment, or injury whether to his person, property, or rights through the unlawful act, omission, or negligence of another.

Data — Facts, numbers, and information used as a basis for reasoning, discussion, or calculation.

Dead Load — Weight of the structure, structural members, building components, and any other feature permanently attached to the building that is constant and immobile. Load on a structure due to its own weight and other fixed weights.

Decomposition — Chemical change in which a substance breaks down into two or more simpler substances. Result of oxygen acting on a material that results in a change in the material's composition. Oxidation occurs slowly, sometimes resulting in the rusting of metals.

Decontaminate — To remove a foreign substance that could cause harm; frequently used to describe removal of a hazardous material from the person, clothing, or area.

Defamation — Publication of anything that injures the good name or reputation of a person or brings disrepute to a person.

Deflagration — (1) Chemical reaction producing vigorous heat and sparks or flame and moving through the material (as black or smokeless powder) at less than the speed of sound. A major difference among explosives is the speed of the reaction. (2) Can also refer to intense burning, a characteristic of Class B explosives. (3) An explosion involving a chemical reaction in which the reaction (energy front) proceeds at less than the speed of sound.

Deposition — Sworn testimony taken out of court.

Detonation — (1) Supersonic thermal decomposition, which is accompanied by a shock wave in the decomposing material. (2) Explosion with an energy front that travels faster than the speed of sound.

Direct Evidence — Refers to facts that are learned through use of the five senses.

Dust Explosion — Rapid burning (deflagration), with explosive force, of any combustible dust. Dust explosions generally are two explosions: a small explosion or shock wave creates additional dust in an atmosphere causing the second and larger explosion.

E

Electric Arc — Visible discharge of electricity across a gap or between electrodes.

Electrical Heat Energy — Heat energy that is electrical in origin including resistance heating, dielectric heating, heat from arcing, and heat from static electricity. Poorly maintained electrical appliances, exposed wiring, and lightning are sources of electrical heat energies.

Endothermic Heat Reaction — Chemical reaction in which a substance absorbs heat energy.

Evidence — (1) One of three requirements of evaluation. The information, data, or observation that allows the instructor to compare what was expected to what actually occurred. (2) In law, something legally presented in court that bears on the point in question. (3) Information collected and analyzed by an investigator.

Exclusionary Evidence — Information collected to show that a particular device or scenario can be ruled out with relation to the ignition or fire spread scenario.

Exclusionary Rule — Judicially established evidentiary rule that excludes from admission at trial evidence seized in a manner considered unreasonable within the meaning of the Fourth Amendment of the U.S. Constitution.

Exigent Circumstance — Emergency situation requiring immediate action to prevent imminent danger to life or serious damage to property, or to prevent the destruction of evidence.

Exothermic Reaction — Chemical reaction between two or more materials that changes the materials and produces heat, flames, and toxic smoke.

Expert Witness — Person who has specialized knowledge in a particular field through specialized skill, expertise, training and/or education and is adjudged qualified to render expert opinions in that field in court proceedings.

Explosion — A physical or chemical process that results in the rapid release of high pressure gas into the environment.

Explosion-Proof Equipment — Equipment that is in a rigidly build container so it withstands an internal explosion and prevents ignition of a surrounding flammable atmosphere; designed so it will not provide an ignition source in an explosive atmosphere.

Explosive — (1) Any material or mixture that will undergo an extremely fast, self-propagation reaction when subjected to some form of energy. (2) Materials capable of burning or bursting suddenly and violently.

Explosive Range — Range between the upper and lower flammable limits of a substance.

F

Fahrenheit Scale — Temperature scale on which the freezing point is 32°F (0°C) and the boiling point at sea level is 212°F (100°C) at normal atmospheric pressure.

Fire — Rapid oxidation of combustible materials accompanied by a release of energy in the form of heat and light.

Fire Alarm Signaling System — (1) System of alerting devices that takes a signal from fire detection, manually activated devices, or extinguishing equipment and alerts building occupants or proper authorities of a fire condition. (2) System used to dispatch fire department personnel and apparatus to emergency incidents.

Fire Behavior — (1) Manner in which fuel ignites, flames develop, and heat and fire spread; sometimes used to refer to the characteristics of a particular fire. (2) Manner in which a fire reacts to the variables of fuel, weather, and topography.

Fire Cause — (1) Agency or circumstance that started a fire or set the stage for one to start; source of a fire's ignition. (2) The sequence of events that allows the source of ignition and the fuel to come together. (3) The combination of fuel supply, heat source, and a hazardous act that results in a fire.

Fire Cause Determination — Process of establishing the cause of a fire incident through careful investigation and analysis of the available evidence.

Fire Hazard — Any material, condition, or act that contributes to the start of a fire or that increases the extent or severity of fire.

Fire Load — The amount of fuel within a compartment expressed in pounds per square foot obtained by dividing the amount of fuel present by the floor area. Fire load is used as a measure of the potential heat release of a fire within a compartment.

Fire Patterns — Visible or measurable physical effects that remain after a fire.

Fire Perimeter — Edge of a natural cover fire.

Flame — Light of various colors given off by burning gases or vapors during the combustion process. Visible, luminous body of a burning gas.

Flameover — Condition that occurs when a portion of the fire gases trapped at the upper level of a room ignite, spreading flame across the ceiling of the room.

Flame Spread — Movement of a flame away from the ignition source.

Flammable — Capable of burning and producing flames.

Flammable and Explosive Limits — The upper and lower concentrations of a vapor expressed in percent mixture with an oxidizer that will produce a flame at a given temperature and pressure.

Flammable Liquid — Any liquid having a flash point below 100°F (37.8°C) and having a vapor pressure not exceeding 40 psi absolute (280 kPa).

Flammable Range — The range between the upper flammable limit and lower flammable limit in which a substance can be ignited. Also called Explosive Range.

Flammable Solids — Solid materials other than explosives that are liable to cause fires through friction or retained heat from manufacturing or processing or that ignite readily and then burn vigorously and persistently, creating a serious transportation hazard.

Flashover — Stage of a fire at which all surfaces and objects within a space have been heated to their ignition temperature and flame breaks out almost at once over the surface of all objects in the space.

Flash Point — Minimum temperature at which a liquid gives off enough vapors to form an ignitable mixture with air near the liquid's surface.

Floor Plan — Architectural drawing showing the layout of a floor within a building as seen from above. It outlines the location and function of each room.

Forensic Science — Application of scientific procedures to the interpretation of physical events such as those that occur at a fire scene; the art of reconstructing past events and then explaining that process and one's findings to investigators and triers of fact; criminalistics.

Fully Involved — When an entire area of a building is completely involved in heat and flame.

G

Gamma Radiation — Electromagnetic wave with no electrical charge. This type of radiation is extremely penetrating; very high energy X-rays.

Gas — Compressible substance, with no specific volume, that tends to assume the shape of a container. Molecules move about most rapidly in this state.

Gas-Sensing Detector — Detection and alarm device that uses either a semiconductor principle or a catalytic-element principle to detect fire gases.

Gross Negligence — willful and wanton disregard.

H

Hazard — Condition, substance, or device that can directly cause injury or loss; the source of a risk.

Hazard Area — Established area from which bystanders and unneeded rescue workers are prohibited.

Hazardous Atmosphere — Atmosphere that may or may not be immediately dangerous to life and health but that is oxygen deficient, that contains a toxic or disease-producing contaminant, or that contains a flammable or explosive vapor or gas.

Hazardous Material — (1) Any material that poses an unreasonable risk to the health and safety of persons and/or the environment if it is not properly controlled during handling, storage, manufacture, processing, packaging, use, disposal, or transportation. (2) Substances or materials in quantities or forms that may pose an unreasonable risk to health, safety, or property when stored, transported, or used in commerce (DOT).

Heat — Form of energy associated with the motion of atoms or molecules in solids or liquids that is transferred from one body to another as a result of a temperature difference between the bodies such as from the sun to the earth. To signify its intensity, it is measured in degrees of temperature.

Heat of Combustion — Total amount of thermal energy (heat) that could be generated by the combustion (oxidation) reaction if a fuel were completely burned. The heat of combustion is measured in British Thermal Units (Btu) per pound or calories per gram.

Heat of Decomposition — Release of heat from decomposing compounds, usually due to bacterial action.

Heat Release Rate (HRR) — Total amount of heat produced or released to the atmosphere from the convective-lift fire phase of a fire per unit mass of fuel consumed per unit time.

Hot Smoldering Phase — Phase or stage of fire in which the level of oxygen in a confined space is below that needed for flaming combustion; characterized by glowing embers, high heat at all levels of the room, and heavy smoke and fire gas production.

Hypothesis — Explanation designed to explain certain observations that have not yet been tested.

I

ICC — (1) Abbreviation for International Code Council. (2) Abbreviation for the former Interstate Commerce Commission; now the U.S. Department of Transportation.

IDLH — Abbreviation for Immediately Dangerous to Life and Health.

Ignition — Beginning of flame propagation or burning; the start of a fire.

Ignition Source — The mechanism or initial energy source employed to initiate combustion such as a spark that provides a means for the initiation of self-sustained combustion.

Ignition Stage (Incipient Phase) — First phase of the burning process where the substance being oxidized is producing some heat, but it has not spread to other substances nearby. During this stage, the oxygen content of the air has not been significantly reduced.

Ignition Temperature — Minimum temperature to which a fuel (other than a liquid) in air must be heated in order to start self-sustained combustion independent of the heating source.

IMS — Abbreviation for Incident Management System.

Incendiary — (1) An incendiary agent such as a bomb. (2) A fire deliberately set under circumstances in which the responsible party knows it should not be ignited. (3) Relating to or involving a deliberate burning of property.

Incendiary Device — Contrivance designed and used to start a fire.

Incident Commander (IC) — Person in charge of the Incident Management System and responsible for the management of all incident operations during an emergency.

Incident Investigation — Act of investigating or gathering data to determine the factors that contributed to a fatality, injury, or property loss or to determine fire cause and origin.

Incident Management System — System described in NFPA 1561, *Standard on Fire Department Incident Management System*, that defines the roles, responsibilities, and standard operating procedures used to manage emergency operations. Such systems may also be referred to as Incident Command Systems (ICS).

Incipient Phase — First phase of the burning process in a confined space in which the substance being oxidized is producing some heat, but the heat has not spread to other substances nearby. During this phase, the oxygen content of the air has not been significantly reduced.

Interrogation — A formal line of questioning of an individual who is suspected of committing a crime or who may be reluctant to provide answers to the investigator's questions.

Investigation — An official inquiry.

J

Jurisdiction — (1) Legal authority to operate or function. (2) Boundaries of a legally constituted entity.

K

Kilowatt (KW) — Measurement of rate of heat release measured in the number of Btus per second (equivalent to ten 100-watt light bulbs).

L

Latent Heat of Vaporization — Quantity of heat absorbed by a substance at the point at which it changes from a liquid to a vapor.

Law — Rules of conduct that are adopted and enforced by an authority having jurisdiction that guide society's actions. There are three types of laws: legislative, administrative, judiciary.

Law of Conservation of Mass — Theory that states that mass is neither created nor destroyed in any ordinary chemical reaction; mass that is lost is converted into energy in the form of heat and light.

Law of Heat Flow — Natural law that specifies that heat tends to flow from hot substances to cold substances. This phenomenon is based on the supposition that one substance can absorb heat from another.

Liability — All types of debts and obligations one is bound in justice to perform; a condition of being responsible for a possible or actual loss, penalty, evil, expense, or burden; a condition that creates a duty to perform an act immediately or in the future.

Liquid — A substance with a constant volume that assumes the shape of its container. The molecules flow freely, but substantial cohesion prevents them from expanding as a gas would.

Load — (1) The sum of the wattages of the various devices being served by a circuit. (2) Any effect that a structure must be designed to resist. Forces of loads, such as gravity, wind, earthquakes, and soil pressure, are exerted on a building.

Lower Explosive Limit (LEL) — Lowest percentage of fuel/oxygen mixture required to support combustion. Any mixture with a lower percentage would be considered "too lean" to burn.

Lower Flammable Limit (LFL) — Lower limit at which a flammable gas or vapor will ignite; below this limit the gas or vapor is too lean or thin to burn (too much oxygen and not enough gas).

M

Malicious — Often an element of arson; state requirements may vary, but often this state of mind is in the nature of intending to injure, vex, or annoy another person, to commit an unlawful act, and occasionally a wish to defraud.

Material First Ignited — The fuel that is first set on fire by the heat of ignition. To be meaningful, both a type of material and a form of material should be identified.

Material Safety Data Sheet (MSDS) — Form provided by the manufacturer and blender of chemicals that contains information about chemical composition, physical and chemical properties, health and safety hazards, emergency response procedures, and waste disposal procedures of the specified material.

Molotov Cocktail — Crude bomb made of a breakable container such as a bottle filled with a flammable liquid and usually fitted with a wick that is ignited just before the bottle is hurled, creating a fire bomb.

Motivation — Internal process, arousal and maintenance of behavior, in which energy is produced by needs or expended in the direction of goals. Motivation usually occurs in someone who is interested in achieving some goal.

Multiple Points of Origin — Two or more separate points of fire origin discovered at a fire scene giving a strong indication of arson.

N

National Fire Protection Association (NFPA) — Nonprofit educational and technical association devoted to protecting life and property from fire by developing fire protection standards and educating the public.

Negligence — Breach of duty where there is a responsibility to perform or conduct that fails to meet the standard of care required by the law or that would be expected of a reasonable and prudent person under like circumstances.

Nonflammable — Incapable of combustion under normal circumstances; normally used when referring to liquids or gases.

O

Observation — Actually seeing or watching a person's behavior in a natural setting.

Occupancy — (1) General fire service term for a building, structure, or residency. (2) Building code classification based on the use to which owners or tenants put buildings or portions of buildings. Regulated by the various building and fire codes.

Ordinance — Local or municipal law that applies to persons and things of the local jurisdiction; a local agency act that has the force of a statute; different from law that is enacted by federal or state/provincial legislatures.

Overhaul — Those operations conducted once the main body of fire has been extinguished that consist of searching for and extinguishing hidden or remaining fire, placing the building and its contents in a safe condition, determining the cause of the fire, and recognizing and preserving evidence of arson.

Oxygen-Deficient Atmosphere — Any atmosphere containing less than the normal 21 percent oxygen found in atmospheric air. At least 16 percent oxygen is needed for flame production and human life.

P

Pattern — Distinctive markings left on a structure or contents after a fire.

Perimeter Control — Establishing and maintaining control of the outer edge or boundary of an incident scene.

Personal Protective Equipment (PPE) — General term for the equipment worn by firefighters and rescuers; includes helmets, coats, pants, boots, eye protection, gloves, protective hoods, self-contained breathing apparatus, and personal alert safety systems (PASS devices). Also called Bunker Clothes, Protective Clothing, Turnout Clothing, or Turnout Gear.

Physical Properties — Those properties that do not involve a change in the chemical identity of the substance. However, they affect the physical behavior of the material inside and outside the container, which involves the change of the state of the material; for example, the Boiling Point, the Specific Gravity, the Vapor Density, and Water Solubility.

Placard — Diamond-shaped sign that is affixed to each side of a structure or a vehicle transporting hazardous materials to inform responders of fire hazards, life hazards, special hazards, and reactivity potential. Required on containers that are 640 cubic feet (18 m3) or larger.

Point of Origin — Exact physical location where the heat source and fuel come in contact with each other and a fire begins.

Proximate Cause — (1) One that in a naturally continuous sequence produces the injury, and without which the result would not have occurred. (2) That which (an act), in a natural and continuous sequence unbroken by any intervening cause, produces injury, and without which (the act) the result would not have occurred.

Pyrolysis (Pyrolysis Process or Sublimation) — Thermal or chemical decomposition of fuel (matter) because of heat that generally results in the lowered ignition temperature of the material. The pre-ignition combustion phase of burning during which heat energy is absorbed by the fuel, which in turn gives off flammable tars, pitches, and gases. Pyrolysis of wood releases combustible gases and leaves a charred surface.

Pyromania — Uncontrollable impulse to set fires.

R

Radiation — (1) The transmission or transfer of heat energy from one body to another body at a lower temperature through intervening space by electromagnetic waves such as infrared thermal waves, radio waves, or X rays. Also called Radiated Heat. (2) Energy from a radioactive source emitted in the form of waves or particles.

Radioactive Particles — Particles emitted during the process of radioactive decay. There are three types of radioactive particles: alpha, beta, and gamma.

Rate of Spread (ROS) — Relative activity of a fire in extending its horizontal dimensions. Expressed as rate of increase of the total perimeter of a fire, as rate of forward spread of the fire front, or as rate of increase in area, depending on the intended use of the information. Usually expressed in chains or acres (hectares) per hour for a specific period in the fire's history.

Rate of Vaporization — The speed at which a liquid evaporates or vaporizes.

Rekindle — Reignition of a fire because of latent heat, sparks, or smoldering embers; can be prevented by proper overhaul.

Resistance Heating — Heat generated by passing an electrical current through a conductor such as a wire or an appliance.

Rollover — Condition in which the unburned combustible gases released in a confined space (such as a room or aircraft cabin) during the incipient or early steady-state phase accumulate at the ceiling level. These superheated gases are pushed, under pressure, away from the fire area and into uninvolved areas where they mix with oxygen. When their flammable range is reached and additional oxygen is supplied by opening doors and/or applying fog streams, they ignite and a fire front develops, expanding very rapidly in a rolling action across the ceiling.

Safety Officer — (1) Fire officer whose primary function is to administrate safety within the entire scope of fire department operations. Also referred to as the Health and Safety Officer. (2) Member of the IMS Command Staff responsible to the incident commander for monitoring and assessing hazardous and unsafe conditions and developing measures for assessing personnel safety on an incident. Also referred to as the Incident Safety Officer.

Scene Assessment — Initial observation and evaluation of an emergency scene; related more to incident stabilization than to problem mitigation.

Size-Up — Ongoing mental evaluation process performed by the operational officer in charge of an incident that enables him or her to determine and evaluate all existing influencing factors that are used to develop objectives, strategy, and tactics for fire suppression before committing personnel and equipment to a course of action.

Specific Heat — The amount of heat required to raise the temperature of a specified quantity of a material and the amount of heat necessary to raise the temperature of an identical amount of water by the same number of degrees.

Resistance — The opposition to the flow of an electric current in a conductor or component. Measured in ohms (Ω).

Resistance Heating — Heat generated by passing an electrical current through a conductor such as a wire or an appliance.

Rollover — Condition in which the unburned combustible gases released in a confined space during the incipient or early steady-state phase accumulate at the ceiling level. These superheated gases are pushed, under pressure, away from the fire area and into uninvolved areas where they mix with oxygen. When their flammable range is reached and additional oxygen is supplied by opening doors and/or applying fog streams, they ignite and a fire front develops, expanding very rapidly in a rolling action across the ceiling.

S

Size-Up — Ongoing mental evaluation process performed by the operational officer in charge of an incident that enables him or her to determine and evaluate all existing influencing factors that are used to develop objectives, strategy, and tactics for fire suppression before committing personnel and equipment to a course of action.

Scientific Method — The systematic pursuit of knowledge involving the recognition and formulation of a problem, the collection of data through observation and experiment, and the formulation and testing of a hypothesis.

Smoke — Visible products of combustion resulting from the incomplete combustion of carbonaceous materials and composed of small particles of carbon, tarry particles, and condensed water vapor suspended in the atmosphere, which vary in color and density depending on the types of material burning and the amount of oxygen.

Solar Heat Energy — Energy transmitted from the sun in the form of electromagnetic radiation.

Specific Gravity — Weight of a substance compared to the weight of an equal volume of water at a given temperature. A specific gravity less than 1 indicates a substance lighter than water; a specific gravity greater than 1 indicates a substance heavier than water.

Specific Heat — The amount of heat required to raise the temperature of a specified quantity of a material and the amount of heat necessary to raise the temperature of an identical amount of water by the same number of degrees.

Spark — Small bit of solid material heated to incandescence.

Spoliation — Loss, destruction or material alteration of a object or document that is evidence or potential evidence in a legal proceeding, by one who has the responsibility for its preservation.

Spontaneous Heating — Heating resulting from chemical or bacterial action in combustible materials that may lead to spontaneous ignition.

Spontaneous Ignition — Combustion of a material initiated by an internal chemical or biological reaction producing enough heat to cause the material to ignite. Also called spontaneous combustion.

Standard — Criterion documents that are developed to serve as models or examples of desired performance or behaviors and that contain requirements and specifications outlining minimum levels of performance, protection, or construction. No one is required to meet the requirements set forth in standards unless those standards are legally adopted by the authority having jurisdiction, in which case they become law.

Static Electricity — Accumulation of electrical charges on opposing surfaces created by the separation of unlike materials or by the movement of surfaces.

Steady-State Burning Phase — (1) Generally considered the phase of the fire where sufficient oxygen and fuel are available for fire growth and open burning to a point where total involvement is possible. (2) The phase in a fire when the rate of heat release is constant with respect to time.

Structure Hazard Assessment — Assessment performed by structural engineer and hazardous materials specialist to determine the current condition of the structure.

Surface-To-Mass Ratio — The ratio of the surface area of the fuel to the mass of the fuel.

T

Tetrahedron — In fire science, a tetrahedron is used to represent the flaming mode of combustion consisting of fuel, heat, oxygen, and the uninhibited chain reaction.

Thermal Layering (of Gases) — Outcome of combustion in a confined space in which gases tend to form into layers, according to temperature, with the hottest gases found at the ceiling and the coolest gases at floor level. Also called Thermal Balance or Heat Stratification.

Tort — Private or civil wrong or injury, including action for bad faith breach of contract, resulting from breach of duty that is based on society's expectations regarding interpersonal conduct; a violation of a duty imposed by general law upon all persons in a relationship that involves a given transaction.

Toxic Atmosphere — Any area, inside or outside a structure, where the air is contaminated by a poisonous substance that may be harmful to human life or health if it is inhaled, swallowed, or absorbed through the skin.

Toxic Gas — A poisonous gas that contains poisons or toxins that are hazardous to life. For example, many gaseous products of combustion are poisonous and toxic materials generally give off poisonous vapors when exposed to an intensely heated environment.

Trailer — Combustible material, such as rolled rags, blankets, newspapers, or flammable liquid, often used in intentionally set fires to connect remote fuel packages (combustible materials, pools of ignitable liquid, etc.) in order to spread fire from one point or area to other points or areas. Frequently used in conjunction with an incendiary device.

Transmission of Heat — Flow of heat by conduction, convection, or radiation.

U

Under Control — Term used to describe the point in a fire incident when the fire's progress has been stopped. Final extinguishment and overhaul can begin at this time.

Unity of Command — Organizational principle in which workers report to only one supervisor in order to eliminate conflicting orders and the confusion that would result.

Upper Explosive Limit (UEL) — Maximum concentration of vapor or gas in air that will allow combustion to occur. Concentrations above this are called "too rich" to burn.

V

Vaporization — Process of evolution that changes a liquid into a gaseous state. The rate of vaporization depends on the substance involved, heat, and pressure.

Ventilation — Systematic removal of heated air, smoke, gases or other airborne contaminants from a structure and replacing them with cooler and/or fresher air to reduce damage and to facilitate fire fighting operations.

Vertical Ventilation — Ventilating at the highest point of a building through existing or created openings and channeling the contaminated atmosphere vertically within the structure and out the top. Done with holes in the roof, skylights, roof vents, or roof doors. Also called Top Ventilation.

V-Pattern — Characteristic cone-shaped fire pattern left by fire on a wall at or near the point of origin.

W

Wildfire — Unplanned, unwanted, and uncontrolled fire involving vegetative fuels that often threatens structures.

Index

at structural fires, 69
at vehicle fires, 72-74
International System of Units (SI), 39, 40, 41
interviews, conducting, 29 , 30 , 67-68
intrusion systems, noting condition of, 29
investigations
    ERP roles and responsibilities, 65
    goals of, 1-2
    search and seizure issues, 131-133
investigators
    conducting independent investigations, 33-34
    guidelines for calling in, 26 , 31
    insurance adjusters contracting with, 33
iron oxide (rust), 44

J

joules, measuring energy using, 40
juvenile firesetters, 93-96

K

kilowatts (kW joules/sec), 41 , 59
kits used for preserving evidence, 108-110

L

law enforcement
    cordoning scenes and, 31
    crowd control assistance, 19
    guidelines for, 26
    intervention programs involving, 96
    investigation of explosions involving, 86
    personal security and, 19
Law of Conservation of Mass, 60
legal issues
    ERP roles and responsibilities, 34 35
    independent investigations, 33
    safety issues, 21-22
    search and seizure, 34, 131-133
length, measurement systems for, 40
lighters found at scenes, 115, 116
lighting at incidents, 17
lightning as ignition source, 81-82, 88
linseed oil-soaked rags self-heating (spontaneous heating), 49-50
liquefied petroleum gas (LPG) hazards, 20
liquid fuels
    in fire tetrahedron, 46-48
    as ignition sources, 83
liquids (aerosols) as products of combustion, 60
liquids found at scenes, preserving, 112, 113, 114
location of fires indicating firesetter motives
    crime concealment, 99
    crisis, 94
    curiosity, 94
    delinquency, 95
    extremism (terrorism), 101
    profit (fraud), 98
    revenge, 97
    vandalism, 97-98
log of evidence. see chain of custody of evidence
loss control and respiratory protection, 9
low explosives, 86, 87
lower flammable limit (LFL), 48
LPG (liquefied petroleum gas) hazards, 20

M

maps used to document scene, 115-118
mass, measurement systems for, 40

matches, 80, 114
material first ignited, 82-85. see also origin of fires
material safety data sheets (MSDS), 11, 12
materials saturated with liquids, 113
measurement systems, 39-40
measuring evidence found at scenes, 118
mechanical heat energy, 51
media, making statements to, 30
medical treatment for animal bites, 19
mental health professionals, intervention programs involving, 96
Miranda warnings, 34
modified equipment found at scenes, 115
Molotov cocktails
    extremists (terrorists) using, 101
    found at scenes, 114
    revenge firesetters using, 97
    strategic firesetters using, 96
motivations for firesetters. see firesetters, motives
MSDS (material safety data sheets), 11, 12
multiple agency incidents, 26

N

National Fire Protection Association. see NFPA (National Fire Protection Association)
National Incident Management System (NIMS), 14
natural classification of fire cause, 79
natural gas, 20, 88
natural sources of ignition, 81-82
NFPA (National Fire Protection Association) contact information, 6
NFPA (National Fire Protection Association) standards
    54 (*Natural Fuel Gas Code*), 20
    704 (*Standard System for the Identification of the Hazards of Materials for Emergency Response*), 11-12
    921 (*Guide for Fire and Explosion Investigations*)
            conducting interviews, 68
            legal issues, 35
            material first ignited, 82
            origin of fires, 65, 67
            spoliation guidelines, 34, 106, 107
    1971 (*Standard on Protective Ensemble for Structural Fire Fighting*), 6, 7, 8
    1975 (*Standard on Station/Work Uniforms for Fire and Emergency Services*), 7
nonpiloted ignition, 52
notes. see documentation; reports
nuclear heat energy, 51

O

occupancies, observations of type and condition, 28. see also *specific types of occupancies*
occupants
    interviewing, 29 , 30 , 67
    survival of, 58
Occupational Safety and Health Administration (OSHA) regulations
    biohazards (29 *CFR* 1910.1030), 14
    electricity and electrical hazards (29 *CFR* 1910.331), 20
    helmets and hard hats, 7
    importance of conforming to, 5
OH&S (Canadian Centre for Occupational Health and Safety), 7
oily rags found at scenes, 115
on-scene reports, 28
open flames as ignition sources, 80
orientation (position) of fuels, 46, 47, 82
origin of fires. see also material first ignited; *topics generally in this index*

hazards of, 61
initial observations of ERP, 28
smoking materials as ignition sources, 79-80, 89
solid fuels
in fire tetrahedron, 46
as ignition sources, 83
sparks and arcs as ignition sources, 80-81, 84
special investigation units, roles and responsibilities, 33
speed, measurement systems for, 40
spoliation of evidence. *see also* evidence, preserving
defined, 25
described, 106
ERPs and legal issues, 34-35
NFPA guidelines on, 106, 107
spontaneous heating (self-heating), 49-50, 82
spread of fires
during growth stage of fire development, 53, 69
heat and, 60-61
position of solid fuels and, 46, 47
sprinkler system hazards, 21
state agencies. *see also* legal issues; *specific agencies*
organizations interested in fire cause, 125-130
roles and responsibilities, 34
statements about investigations, avoiding premature judgment, 30
static electricity as ignition source, 81
strategic firesetting, 95-96
stream patterns, noting for post-suppression activities, 29
stress as motive for firesetting, 94-95
structural collapse and water hazards, 21
structural fire fighting gear. *see* personal protective equipment (PPE)
structural stability, 16
structure fires
evidence gathering and evaluation, 68-70
steps in determining origin of fires, 65
sun, heat energy produced by, 51, 81
suppression operations
evidence preservation and, 71, 110-111
observations of ERP during, 29
surface-to-mass ratio of fuels, 46, 82
surface-to-volume ratio of fuels, 48
surveying equipment used to document scene, 117, 118
suspicious fires, 79
Systeme International (SI), 39, 40, 41

T
target fuels, 60
temperature
development of fires and, 53, 59
flammable range and, 48
as indicator of heat, 40
protection from, 7 , 11
structural stability and, 16
terrorism as motive for firesetting, 100-101
thermal radiation, 42, 43
timing devices found at scenes, 114
tire tracks and footprints, preserving, 113
total fire loss, 69, 70
toxic fire gases, 60
trailers found at scenes, 114
training, PPE use included in, 6
transfer of heat, 41-42
turnout clothing, 7

U
unconfined fires, development of, 52
undetermined classification of fire cause, 79
Uniform Crime Reports, 93
upper flammable limit (UFL), 48
U.S. Department of Homeland Security, 14
U.S. Department of Justice (DOJ) providing investigation assistance, 34
U.S. Department of Transportation (DOT), 11
U.S. Environmental Protection Agency guidelines, 5
U.S. Federal Bureau of Investigation statistics on juveniles as firesetters, 93
U.S. Federal Emergency Management Agency (FEMA), 14
U.S. Occupational Safety and Health Administration. *see* Occupational Safety and Health Administration (OSHA) regulations
utility companies, roles and responsibilities, 34
utility systems
hazards involving, 19-21
securing, 29

V
vandalism as motive for firesetting, 97
vanity as motive for firesetting, 99-100
vaporization, 46-48, 50
vegetation fires (wildfires), 75, 88-89
vehicle fires, evidence gathering and evaluation, 70-74
vehicles at the scene, 28
ventilation
described, 18
development of fires and, 58, 59
noting for post-suppression activities, 29
reducing backdraft potential, 60
ventilation controlled fires, 52
victims of incidents
at crime scenes, 27
photographing, 120-123
smoke and, 61
taking note of, 28
volume
of compartments, 59
measurement systems for, 40

W
walls
area of origin indicators, 69
development of fires and, 52-53, 54
water
endothermic reactions and, 44
hazards involving, 16 , 21
vaporization and, 46-47
weather. *see* temperature; wind hazards
weight, measurement systems for, 40
wildfires, 75, 88-89
wind hazards, 16 , 28
witnesses of incidents
interviewing, 29 , 67
photographing, 119
taking note of, 28 , 99-100
wood as fuel, 46
work, measurement systems for, 40

Indexed by Kari Kells